7/6

H. S. Kirby.

1952

D1349073

By the same Author

TEN YEARS UNDER THE EARTH

MY CAVES

THE AUTHOR

MY CAVES

by

NORBERT CASTERET

Translated by
R. L. G. Irving

*With 26 illustrations
in photogravure*

LONDON
J. M. DENT & SONS LTD.

J. M. DENT & SONS LTD.
Aldine House · Bedford St. · London

Made in Great Britain
by
The Temple Press · Letchworth · Herts
First published 1947

INTRODUCTION

THIS book is a sequel to the story of my campaigns underground contained in *Dix ans sous terre* and *Au fond des gouffres*. Those earlier works set out the most important of my explorations, discoveries, and researches, and this third volume continues the tale of my subsequent labours and adventures under the earth.

My natural preference, as well as my isolation up here in the depths of the country, on the outskirts of a wood and in full view of the Pyrenees, makes the portals of caves more inviting to me than those of libraries; the work I love best is the great book of nature.

Everything I have described has been observed in caves in the Pyrenees. I make no sort of claim to ownership or exclusive use of them, but in many cases I have discovered them (sometimes I have even had to clear the way in with my own hands), explored them, and studied them. Visits to seven hundred caves or pot-holes, a life given up wholly to the study of them, and a very appreciable portion of that life spent actually underground are, I think, a justification for the title I have given to this book. It is not a spelaeologist's handbook nor is it a compendium of the knowledge which has accumulated on a subject so immense in range and as yet so imperfectly understood. All I set out to do here is to tell some tales of exploration and adventure, to describe my own rather rudimentary equipment and my methods of using it, and to pass on some of the secrets of the mysterious regions under the ground we tread.

You will find in these pages neither theories nor technical dissertations on the geology of caves, but simply what I go underground to find and think about; subjects for personal investigation, scenery reminiscent of Dante, new and thrilling sensations, violent physical exertions too, often involving acrobatics, occasionally perilous, for, as Voiture has said: 'Le vrai secret pour avoir de la santé et de la gaieté, est que le corps soit agité et que l'esprit se repose.' Or, as Shelley puts it in fewer and finer words: 'The happiness of the soul is in action.'

The lone wanderer in these places below the surface has joys beside those of action, the calm complete silence, the solitude in superb surroundings which conduce to quiet thought and the uplifting of the mind.

My explorations in caves have not been made with a view to writing books about them, but my frequent visits to this particular domain, too little known in my opinion, one might almost say unknown, have impelled me to try and make it better known and loved.

It is to pay my debt to the underground world for the unforgettable hours I have lived in it, for the wonders it has revealed and the emotions it has stirred that I have written *Mes cavernes*.

N. C.

TRANSLATOR'S NOTE

EXPLORING in the bowels of the earth might seem to have little in common with mountaineering. It is a fact, however, that most of the daring work done in discovering the interesting secrets buried in deep caves has been initiated and carried out by men who were mountaineers. Did not the great climber A. F. Mummery write: 'I myself should still climb . . . even if the only climbing attainable were the dark and gruesome pot-holes of the Yorkshire Dales.'

And, after all, much of the hard work is mountaineering in reverse: the ascent follows the descent instead of preceding it. Some of M. Norbert Casteret's climbs on the damp walls of caves, in complete darkness but for the glimmer of a torch, would, I think, be creditable performances under the open sky on the rocks of Tryfaen or Scafell.

In England cave exploration has not been taken as seriously as on the Continent. The 'spelaeologist' in English descriptions, certainly in climbing journals, is generally an individual who prefers the strait and narrow and muddy way of surmounting a 'cave pitch' to a breezier, more exposed route outside. In France, spelaeology has become a respectable science, and some of the discoveries made in the far deeper and more extensive caves than any we have in Britain have been of great interest and importance; for example, those of prehistoric drawings and sculptures and the true source of the Garonne. M. Norbert Casteret has played a great part in these discoveries.

In the present volume, besides adding to the many exciting adventures contained in a previous work, *Dix ans sous terre*, he has given a clear, detailed description of his methods and equipment, and a fascinating account of his researches on bats. Before reading this chapter of his book few who were not specialists in the subject will have had any suspicion of the interesting study these generally abused creatures provide, both in the extraordinary care nature has shown in the planning and development of their maternal functions and in their remarkable homing instincts.

A translator's task is occasionally rendered difficult owing to the fact that cave exploration is still little more than a diversion for the climber in Britain, while it is a serious pursuit in France. For terms which have acquired official recognition and a definite meaning to spelaeologists have no established equivalent in English. For example, *chatière* represents an orifice just large enough to tempt an explorer to see if he can penetrate it; I have used cat-hole or cat-run as being fairly intelligible. *Siphon* is the French term for a passage in a cave where the roof sinks below the stream—usually icy cold—flowing through it. I have left it as 'siphon.' The author himself will give the reader a description of these two features of underground exploration which will leave him with an appreciation in the flesh more convincing than any single word or phrase could convey. He will wonder how any one dared to follow his nose into such obviously possible imprisonment for life.

I should like to express my thanks to Mr. E. E. Roberts, one of our few well-known pot-holers, for enabling me to remedy some, at least, of my failures to give the proper terms in use by spelaeologists.

R. L. G. IRVING.

WINCHESTER,
October 1947.

CONTENTS

ILLUSTRATIONS

PART ONE

CAVES FROM WITHIN

Ici, dans sa barbarie primitive, la nature n'a su que fendre des blocs et entasser les masses brutes de ses constructions cyclopéennes.

TAINE.

Here, in her primordial savagery, nature has done no more than cleave great rocks and pile up the rough materials for building on a Cyclopean scale.

I

THE UNDERGROUND RIVER OF LABOUICHE

We came then to the desert shore, that never saw man navigate its waters who thereafter knew return.

DANTE, *Purgatorio*, canto i.

In the course of a spelaeological campaign in the Pyrenees in 1908, the explorer É.-A. Martel entered a cave a few miles from Foix. This cave forms the bed of a stream which disappears underground after winding its way through woods and meadows. Martel and his friends followed this subterranean watercourse for several hundred yards and then, to their astonishment, came to a place where it widened out and ran into an underground river of considerable size flowing along a vast unknown gallery.

Pursuing their way down-stream by walking on the strips of sand and gravel at the sides, the party managed to get along for a further three hundred yards till they were stopped by a lowering of the vault to the water level, producing what is known as a siphon. The explorers then turned their steps up-stream towards the source of the river. The sequel will show that after thirty years the actual source remains unknown, no one having yet succeeded in reaching it. But let us continue the story of the exploration. Having returned to the meeting of the waters underground, our spelaeologists got into collapsible boats and went up-stream for some four hundred and fifty yards to a point where difficulties began which compelled them to beat a retreat.

In the following year, 1909, a new expedition tried its luck. It consisted of nine persons variously distributed in five boats. Their explorations proved extremely exciting and all but ended in a tragedy. As happened to the explorers of the famous underground river of the Puits de

3

Padirac, shipwrecks occurred. 'When we came to the low roof at the Narrows,' writes Martel, 'the first boat, which was overloaded, capsized in thirteen feet of water and M. Fournier and M. Dunac, swimming about in the dark, had some difficulty in escaping from their involuntary cold bath. It was then the turn of another boat, which burst both its skins on a sharp rock and sank like a stone under under the weight of Rudaux and Maréchal, who were impeded in their efforts to get free and reach the bank. A lengthy list of people drowned came very near to being written that day.' Three of the luckier ones pushed on their exploration for three hundred yards above the scene of the double shipwreck, but the party had already gone through too much to give them a fair chance, so in the absence of any possible assistance or hope of succour these three, including Dr. Crémadells of Foix, had no choice but to turn back. So far this underground river of Labouiche had disclosed about three-quarters of a mile of its whole course, but lack of time prevented Martel from renewing his attempts at further exploration.

Beset and overwhelmed as he was by countless inquiries and labours in which he took a leading part in France and other countries, he never had an opportunity of returning to Ariège, so the cave, with its reputation enhanced by the shipwrecks, the check to its explorers, and its liability to sudden flooding, was left severely alone and forgotten.

In 1935 a young man named Lagarde had the luck to discover a gallery whose existence had not previously been suspected; this discovery enabled him to walk dryshod above the subterranean watercourse and so by-pass the siphon which had stopped the Martel party in their exploration down-stream. It was an instructive as well as a lucky find, for it provided evidence that the siphon in question was only a few yards in length. Such a discovery did not escape the notice of the Syndicat d'Initiative of Foix, nor of the local explorer and expert on prehistoric times, Mandement, who at once thought out and put into execution a plan for cutting out the siphon which was the cause of the dangerous flooding and of the interdict under which the cave had suffered for so long.

Having accomplished this indispensable preliminary work, M. Mandement set to work methodically to improve access to the river by dams, light bridges, and widening of the tunnel in certain parts. While this work was in progress a group of amateur spelaeologists, provided with rafts, made a tentative exploration up-stream beyond the point already reached by Martel and his collaborators. This new party, which included the Dr. Crémadells who had been a member of Martel's expedition, encountered many obstacles, the most serious being the ascent of a waterfall where the river pours down into a deep lake. Above the waterfall there were more excitements till further progress was hopelessly blocked by a complete 'siphoning' of the river, the roof dipping steeply right under the water. So, thirty years after the first exploration, another party had to beat a retreat, defeated this time by an alliance between rock and water to form an impassable and without doubt a final obstacle to the further penetration of this splendid cave through which they had made their way for a mile and a quarter.

It was at this stage of the exploration of the cave that I began to think of trying in my turn to investigate this underground river, to see if I could push on further and make it disclose the secret of its source.

At the time of my visit to Labouiche I might have profited by the improvements in progress and proceeded in a comfortable boat as far as the point to which the work had advanced, which was about three hundred yards below the waterfall. Partly from inclination, partly as a sort of tribute to my illustrious predecessor Martel, I insisted on piloting myself alone in my tiny pneumatic skiff. In this way I was able to get a better impression of what the earlier exploration must have been, though in places the sight of dams, pontoons, and ladders reminded me that I was not the first man to navigate this river with its succession of impressive vaults above. The fact that I was not its discoverer in no way detracted from the majesty of the place and I felt its charm to the full. Kneeling, as one does in a canoe, I paddled on in my light boat, which glided noiselessly through the water in a stately silence. Only at long intervals a gentle murmuring of the water awakens life in these windless solitudes at a quickening of the current or a small cascade. Leaning over the side I can see the bottom and the rocks projecting from it. Instinctively one's eye tries to catch the startled dash of a trout, the sidling crawl of a crayfish; a vain hope, for these subterranean waters are barren, no creature can live in them.

The extraordinary variations in the height of the vault, at one time so low I had to stoop, at another rising to a vast height, were only equalled by the strange variety of the decorations which nature has worked into the walls. The rocky tunnel that had been dark, bare, and menacing would suddenly delight me with a profusion of stalactitic ornaments hanging from the roof. Here and there, where the walls were not sheer and repellent, they were hollowed into bays and narrow inlets; long ledges of natural formation ran along the edge of the water where the eye had glimpses of what appeared to be creations of dreamland, citadels and mosques with their innumerable clusters of towers and stalagmitic minarets.

At a few points we took the opportunity of landing and visiting some of the galleries and halls which had escaped the destructive zeal of the iconoclasts, the first persons to enter the cave having been the very people who were anxious to safeguard its wonders, while making access to them easier.

Our cruise underground carried us through such a succession of scenic effects that the time spent on it seemed short. Nevertheless the distance covered was considerable, and it gradually became evident that all traces of engineering work had ceased and that I was in the part of the cave that

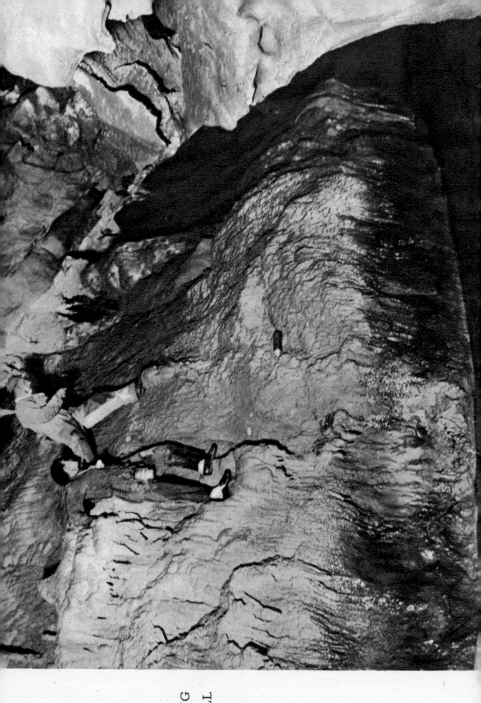

CLIMBING
THE WALL

had only been once seen and traversed by my predecessors. Presently a dull roaring warned us that we were getting close to the waterfall; but sound travels far underground, and I had to paddle quite a long way before coming to the place where the river widens out and the cascade tumbles into it and breaks its placid surface. The noise here becomes deafening and a cold wind produced by the fall blows ceaselessly across the pale-green depths of the pool.

Man had left one more bit of evidence he had been here, the last; a roughly made ladder like a topgallant mast hanging down beside the waterfall. Was it firmly fixed above? Perhaps the rungs were rotten? Carrying my boat in one hand and holding on to the ladder with the other, I climbed up, getting splashed and covered with spray, to the upper sill of the fall. Beyond it the water flows on again peacefully in the tunnel it has made and lined with hard white deposits. I was now only a couple of hundred yards from the siphon at the end, but here the watercourse was very soon interrupted by the curious obstacles called *gours*; they are calcareous partitions characteristic of underground rivers, extremely tiresome to pass, requiring laborious and repeated acrobatics. The boats have to be carried in crossing over these *gours*, and the efforts to get into them again in awkward positions, groping about and balancing in the dark, are apt to end in a ducking. I had had plenty of practice in climbing over these barriers and I took every care not to capsize, but in one of the troughs between I turned right over into the water with every bit of my equipment. Like Martel at Padirac and the first explorers of Labouiche, I too had to pay my tribute to the cave. My only anxiety in the first moment of sudden complete darkness was for my haversack containing among various accessories my camera and a supply of magnesium filings. My electric torch had got wet, and when I got it to work I glanced round to see what damage the shipwreck had done. The boat and paddles were floating sedately in a creek where I could presently go and fetch them; the camera being wrapped in water-proof stuff had not suffered from its immersion. All was well, in fact, except that I was several pounds heavier and my sopping clothes stuck to my body in an icy embrace that was anything but pleasant and would continue so for hours. In addition, my small shipwreck had cost me the loss of an acetylene lamp and a pair of steel climbing irons, which had gone to the bottom. Shivering and feeling rather foolish, like a person who has just had his baptism on his first crossing of the line, I resumed my voyage up-stream, which had now become a sort of water steeple-chase, seeing that I had to jump out of the boat every minute to haul it or carry it, floundering about on sub-merged ledges or the slippery treacherous rims of pools which broke under my weight. In this sorry plight I came at last to the siphon, which is preceded by a short stretch of deep calm water where I could once more paddle along in the usual way.

It was a siphon that made one think hard before tackling it. The low ceiling, with its thick layer of sticky mud left there by floods, dipped deeply under the black water. Bending down I took a long look into the depths whose secrets remained impenetrable by the beam of my torch, and I reflected that on a previous occasion when confronted by a similar obstacle I had not hesitated to dive into the siphon of the Montespan cave. But on that occasion there were compelling reasons for so doing; certain signs as well as observations of my own had given me a premonition of success and urged me on. The discovery of the earliest sculpture in the world has cast a sort of halo round that rather foolishly reckless exploit; and then I had only my-self to think of. After all, the forcing of the passage of a siphon is a dangerous game; it is about an even chance whether you come out of it or not.

For a long time I contemplated this submerged ceiling, and to some purpose, for the next day the siphon was conquered and I had the river running freely in front of

me again, inviting me to pursue my adventure, through
tunnels never entered before.   But that is really another
story. . . .

The following day, in fact, I set off once more upon
the river, but this time there were two of me, if I may so
describe it, for I was followed by a companion equipped
exactly as I was myself, the same helmet, the same trappings
as mine, in a collapsible boat like mine, following in my
wake.   This newly improvised spelaeologist had never
seen the inside of a cave in his life; he was a young man
from Foix whom I had specially noticed for his keenness
and activity and his evident desire to come with me underground.   I certainly never had cause to regret this lapse
from my usual practice of exploring alone; Delteil proved
to be a most capable ally, tough and never worried even
in the most trying experiences and the most unpleasant
situations.   He had, indeed, contracted that sudden and
incurable complaint, spelaeological fever.

Paddling steadily over the calm surface of the river we
reached the waterfall, which thunders down continuously
a mile and a quarter from the entrance of the cave.   On
the way we passed a working party of electricians in a
boat, fixing insulators to the walls.   The sudden appearance of two people sailing along in two rubber skiffs with
a torch in their helmets was such a novel and unexpected
sight that they stopped working and would have watched
us go by in silence if we had not spoken.   Their silent
bewilderment was soon followed by a lively conversation
and expressions of astonishment, and, I rather fancy, by an
explosion of facetious comment at our expense, but we
were a long way past by that time.

It gave me an odd feeling I had never had before to
pass this party working to make a cave accessible to
tourists while we went on to wage a battle, to match our
skill and strength against the unknown difficulties that
suddenly confront those who push their exploration further
and further into the bowels of a mountain.

B

We stopped rowing on reaching the foot of the waterfall, and after a short consultation, with our boats drawn up side by side, we slipped our haversacks off our shoulders and opened them just wide enough to extract certain objects of an obviously fragile nature, for every movement was carried out with the utmost care. Yet our present occupation was a very ordinary, prosaic affair, though it would have greatly astonished a witness of our acts and gestures. if television could have transmitted them to him; we were busy lunching on the water, a mile and a quarter from the light of day!

Before our main effort, before having our provisions crushed to bits in the course of some strenuous climb or sunk in several feet of water, we set to, and made what eventually proved to be the only meal of the day.

The river here ran between vertical walls where landing was impossible, so we thought we might as well lunch afloat, rocked by the wavelets, which made us bob up and down like corks. An occasional stroke of the paddle between mouthfuls was sufficient to prevent our colliding with a stalactite or scraping against a jagged wall which would have imperilled the outer cover of our skiffs, or to get us out of the unpleasant draught blowing down the line of the waterfall.

To any one who is oppressed by the dullness of existence, to the neurasthenic who find each day as hard to endure as the one before, let me recommend spelaeology. It is a sport and a branch of knowledge as well as a diversion, whose pursuit, however much appearances belie the fact, presents widely different and unexpected features, and at the same time calls for all sorts of bodily activity and brings within reach some engrossing subjects for research.

The currents and eddies were rocking us about as they pleased, now driving us together, now apart. I watched my companion as he bobbed about and did honour to our frugal meal. I saw his arm go up and his head go back, helmeted like a warrior of old, with a bottle to his lips as

if he blew a bugle.   A soldier drinking is always a cheerful
sight and the beam of the torch I carried in my helmet lit
up his merry, half-closed eye.   Suddenly he let the bottle
fall and I could see him coughing, throwing himself about,
and choking, for some of the wine had gone down the
wrong way.   But I could hear nothing at all, the noise of
the waterfall drowned every other sound.

Our strange battle of the ships was, however, ended
with our lunch.   We moored them and I began to climb
one of the side walls of the cave.   The solid rock was well
plastered with white calcareous deposit in which short
stalagmites stood out offering tempting but treacherous
hold, for they were as brittle as glass.

It is at this point that my own contribution to the fresh
exploration of the cave begins.   On the previous day I
had come up against the siphon that barred further progress
and had thought long over the problem it presented.
Some sort of cave sense prompted me to look for the solution in the ceiling.   It is an almost invariable rule in
hydrogeology that underground watercourses (which all
start as surface streams) have undergone, in the course of
their evolution, sudden burials and lowerings of their
channels which give rise to a succession of streambeds
one above the other.   In so many caves which have once
provided a passage for a subterranean river, water still
circulating freely has been discovered at the bottom of
deep holes in their lower reaches, that it is only logical,
when confronted with an impracticable siphon like this
one in the underground river of Labouiche, to look above
for the old abandoned streambed, the upper storey which
sometimes provides access to very extensive galleries.
This theory, of whose soundness I had had practical
demonstrations, had persuaded me, on my way back the
day before, to try to climb the side wall where the high
ceiling vanished in darkness.   I had no success, either
because the wall was impossibly steep or because I could
see no opening in the roof.   But as I passed one particular

place, my attention was caught by two suggestive signs; a great sheet of stalagmite, pointing to a previous big flow of water, and a very slight movement of the air, which though barely perceptible suggested a possible passage communicating with unsuspected extensions of the cave.

That is why my attack was now directed on a particular part of the wall a hundred feet below the waterfall, which any one but an expert would have thought precisely similar to the mile or so of wall the cave had already shown him.

I could see my companion was regarding me with secret disapproval and was prepared for inevitable failure, for he betrayed it by an inaction which in him was most unusual.

As I clawed my way slowly up the smooth wall, he settled himself on a ledge to wait, presumably till I gave up the attempt.

Inch by inch, however, I was getting higher, though the holds were almost invisible and far from safe, and a further difficulty, that does not trouble climbers ordinarily, was working in the dark, for the torch in my helmet cast a very inadequate light on only a small portion of the wall, so that I could not stop to examine it either as a whole problem or in detail.

Presently I reached the point I had been aiming at, where the two walls came near enough together for back-and-knee methods. The bits of stalactites I broke off in passing fell down, and the plops they made one after another told me that if I came off I should fall into the river, which was better than being dashed to pieces on rocks.

A tricky overhang had me in momentary difficulties, I might say in distress, and I experienced the fright at the immediate prospect of falling which I had felt on other occasions; a sort of regret, that comes unfortunately too late, for having got into such a critical situation. Distressing moments these, when the muscles maintain their intensest effort, while the mind, far more prompt in action, has already given up the struggle, evokes a vision of the

A FOSSILIZED CASCADE

fall and utters a puerile wail like the child's 'I know I shall never get back.'

The overhang was passed. I then found myself on a sort of terrace which runs horizontally sixty to seventy feet above the river. Moving cautiously forward, it was not long before I found myself directly above the waterfall, whose white foam was the one detail my torch revealed, as I looked down from my high perch as from a fifth-floor balcony.

At this point the terrace turned upwards and was continued in a vertical chimney, up which I could feel a slight draught blowing. My hopes were beginning to take shape and promise fulfilment, but before proceeding to try the ascent of the chimney I had to let Delteil know what I was doing and beg him to have patience. The roar of the waterfall put any conversation out of the question, so I went back along my lofty balcony and leaning over I shouted to him; but I saw his torch much nearer to me than I had thought it could be. Could I possibly have overestimated the height I thought I had climbed? Not a bit of it! My follower had tackled the climb on his own and was grappling with its difficulties at the moment. I did what I could to encourage him by shouts and gestures, but a better way occurred to me, to throw him the rope which was coiled up at the bottom of my rucksack; or rather, which I believed to be there, for I discovered, somewhat late in the day, that it was not there after all. Mishaps like that, and mistakes in tactics, are pretty frequent underground! It was Delteil who had charge of the rope. The beams of both torches were directed on the wall, and I was able to point out the route to my friend, who showed himself a first-rate cragsman, and I was able to give him a bit of help at the overhang.

And now for the chimney. The first thirty feet were fairly simple, but above that a great boss of stalagmite protruded, smooth as a piece of steel armour, compelling us to resort to what climbers call *la courte échelle*; which means that I stood up on Delteil's shoulders while he balanced himself on a ledge. I groped for a handhold of some sort, but there was none. As I hoisted my weight slowly over the rounded boss, relying simply on the friction of my whole body, Delteil seized my feet in his hands and kept pushing me up by the strength of his arms. Then once more I was dependent on my own efforts. I struggled up to the top of the chimney and found it opened out, as my hopes had visualized, into a spacious horizontal gallery where I could take a quick look round.

Here we were, without any doubt, in the old disused bed of the river. Through the chimney we had climbed, and probably through others we should come across later, it had come down and drilled out the lower storey, where it still flows a hundred and thirty feet below its earlier bed. This bed itself must represent only a stage in the constant disappearance of the water in calcareous rocks, a process which geologists call the 'karstic phenomenon.'

The gallery, in places earthy, in others interrupted by a dry *gour*, a sort of petrified wave, runs right above the subterranean river and has the same orientation. After following it down for a hundred feet I came to a great mountain of earth, which had slipped down through some cleft in the ceiling and completely blocked the way.

Turning my steps up the gallery I climbed over an enormous sheet of stalagmite, the succession of great bulges in which showed that a perfect cataract must have come down here. This monumental pile, built up in the past by water saturated with carbonate of lime, rises right up to the roof. A single duct, no wider than a man's head, opens in it and sucks in a violent draught of air with a noise like that made by the bellows of a forge. It was here that our efforts would have to be directed and our future battles fought, for the blowhole widened out beyond the bottle-neck and the intake of air was evidence of the existence of other important cavities awaiting discovery.

Little by little this cave of Labouiche was revealing the

secret working of its hydrogeological system. It gave me a wonderful feeling to be moving forward, tracking out the successive stages in this process. There is a real adventurous thrill in this exploration underground with its revelations of the working of water for thousands of years in the depths of the earth, in a journey through the night of prehistoric ages, suggestive of the time machine of H. G. Wells.

This time I had been careful not to forget the smooth rope, and I let down an end to Delteil who gripped it and hoisted himself up to my level. We were both now in the upper storey of the river system, a storey which, but a moment ago, was only a supposition, but whose existence had been proved to be a reality by our recent hard climb. A spelaeologist's bag of tools should always include a hammer and chisel; they are heavy, cumbersome things, but quite indispensable. Their value was proved now when we set to work to enlarge the opening of the blow-hole. This promised to be no easy job, for it would have to be done lying on the stomach, with my neck twisted round. Moreover, the first blows with the hammer showed the stalagmite to be extremely hard. However, my companion, who had started off by successfully tackling a tricky and exposed bit of climbing, set to work with a will.

Working with the hammer took him back to his craft of cabinet-maker. I was lost in admiration at the mastery he showed. Had it been myself at work, I should have been out of breath by this time and should have infallibly hit myself on the fingers with little to show for it; as it was, I could hear hammer and chisel working away with an admirable rhythm and output. Every now and then the back of a hand pushed back the chippings, flakes of stalagmite, which I collected in a pile in a recess where they could not hamper our snakelike progress, for we were stretched at full length one behind another, in a very low narrow tunnel. From time to time I offered to take my turn and relieve my partner, for it seemed to me he must be quite exhausted, but the only answer he vouchsafed was a sort of low growl.   The hammer kept up its steady blows, the chisel went on ringing, and the debris were pushed back to me with the same automatic movement of the hand.   With a violent wriggle, the miner in front managed to turn over on his back to attack the rocky ceiling without slowing the rhythm of his blows.   This was no man, but a machine!   The chippings which I had treasured with such miserly care became too many to be stuffed into the recess in the wall, so I crawled backwards, making a basket of my arms to gather in all the rubbish and withdrew to make a pile of it further back.   By this time I was feeling rather ashamed of my inaction, so I was glad to become lost in wonder at some amazing plant-like formations of slender stalactites known as eccentric, whose process of growth presents a problem which has so far defeated all the mineralogists.

A hoarse shout from Delteil, who must have swallowed a lot of dust, roused me from my reverie.   He had accumulated such a pile of debris against his body that he could not move.   For the last hour and more he had been working like a black and he still refused to take a rest.   I protested: 'This is too much of a good thing; at any rate, let me see what you have done.'

Passing a man in the narrow gut was no easy matter, but when I had managed to take his place I was lost in admiration.   The cat-hole had been so much enlarged that I believed I could get through.   I had a look first to see the best position to adopt for forcing a passage; then, lying on my back, with one arm stretched out in front and the other close against my body and my shoulders sticking out as little as possible, I began to worm my way along, making a just perceptible advance with each wriggle. Behind me I could hear Delteil protesting that it was still impossible to get through.   I should have found it difficult to answer at the moment, for my bottom was being crushed against the roof while some obstruction was tearing at my shoulder. Nevertheless I was getting through; I was through!

The wretched buttons on my linen overall had taken the skin off my chest; the only mishap at the shoulder was that the stuff had given. My legs were still in the gut, so I took advantage of the fact by asking to have my rucksack hung on to my toe, for by this means it could follow me till I could assume a squatting position or turn round and get hold of it.

This blowhole had given us a bad time, but it did not continue for long as narrow as this first bit, and soon I was able to proceed on all fours and then walk in a normal position in a gallery thirty to forty feet in width. Here I was able to push on my reconnaissance for another two hundred yards to where the gallery ends in a sort of hall embellished with some fine, tall, slender columns. Here the cave narrows again into an earthy kind of gut of repellent aspect, but the draught which blew through it made it quite clear where the line of advance lay. However, the next step was to go back and see how Delteil was getting on. I found him still hammering away to enlarge the cat-hole. In vain I pointed out that he was rather thinner than I was and could certainly get through; he maintained he had tried and failed. That was because he had not gone about it the right way. Both of us were specialists in our own line. I should have taken half a day to chip a passage through with a hammer, whereas he refused to commit himself and force his way through like a worm. He ended by taking my advice, adopting the best position and stretching out an arm on which I exerted a slow steady pull, avoiding any violent jerks. In this way we passed the cat-hole without any damage, if not painlessly, and we both hurried on to the one beyond, which demanded different methods of attack. Here, in fact, we had to burrow in thick, sticky clay which blocked our way and transformed us into huge lumps of mud. Hammer and chisel disappeared in a matrix of clay, while our hands resembled boxing-gloves with a webbing of clay between all the fingers. We became indistinguishable from this horrible slime; siderolithic clay, the geologists call it. Without lingering in this slough, let me just say that we got through it to where the cave opened out again beyond this second gut, which felt rather like a second door of the trap closed behind us.

As we were emerging from this last obstacle and beginning to resume our forward march our ears were struck by a dull rumbling which increased in intensity and then rapidly died down.

Most noises underground seem unusual and we could think of no natural cause to account for what we heard. Our astonishment and our fears soon vanished when we realized that the phenomenon was merely a train. The railway from Foix to Saint-Girons passes right over the cave and the thunder of the heavy train, transmitted through the rails and the limestone rocks, which carry sound well, reached us down below, but what an amazing depth of rock the sound had traversed!

There is in me some sort of kink, no doubt connected with the cave habit, as a result of which I am always being struck by the contrast and the relation of what I am looking at with what I cannot see. I cannot look at a bit of sea or country without thinking of the liquid depths or the subterranean chasms which underlie the blue surface of the water or the smiling landscape. And conversely, when I am deep underground in the potholes and caves in which a considerable part of my life is spent, I find myself trying to picture what is happening and what life there is on the surface directly above the place where I am creeping about like a caterpillar in the realm of silence and of darkness. I picture the train rolling rapidly along through a countryside bathed in sunshine in a pleasant corner of this department of Ariège, where the mountains begin to rise into the high Pyrenees. I can see the passengers sitting at ease, each wrapped in his own thoughts and gently rocked by the motion of the train. And among them all, from first to last, whether his mind is wandering or tensely occupied, whether he is studying the country or deep in a book, is there a single one who imagines that right under his feet, beneath a terrifying depth of earth and rock, two fellow mortals, stranded in some recess of an underground maze that extends for miles, sit calmly chatting as they try to scrape off with their knives the casing of mud that covers them?

At the outset of our voyage of discovery, we had been surprised at the narrowness of the passage we had to force and the obstructions that we met. From now on it was the vast scale of the cavern which amazed us and presented us with new difficulties.

After a descent through a chaos of great boulders we found ourselves wandering in a vast gallery leading to the grandest cascade of stalagmitic rock we had ever seen underground. We climbed this and at the top we came out into another extensive hall presided over by a huge stalagmite like a giant warrior, which we christened on the spot 'Gaston Phébus' in honour of the paladin, the Comte de Foix, whose exploits in Ariège are still related in the history and legends of the country.

Could this be the last great chamber of the cave? We separated to give ourselves a better chance of finding the exit which might lead to further discoveries. My searchings were disclosing nothing but walled-up recesses loaded with stalactites, when I heard a triumphant shout from Delteil. Right at the top end of the chamber, behind the imposing statue of Gaston Phébus and, as it were, mounting guard over it, he had found a cat-hole, the third that day. This one did not hold us back for long. A few vigorous hammer blows quickly dashed to pieces some small limestone columns which could offer but a frail barrier to the vandalism which accompanies a thirst for exploration.

Was each of these bottle-necks to lead us into still vaster hollows in the mountain? Was this cave to become more and more spacious? The proportions of the new

chamber which our torches revealed to our astonished eyes
were colossal; the scenes with which Gustave Doré has
illustrated Dante's *Inferno* convey a better idea of it than
anything else. The chaos of the floor was divided into
two great pits by a cyclopean arch of rock, the Pont du
Diable. Peering up into the vault above, we instinctively
looked for harpies or some lost soul flitting about in its
mysterious recesses; but there was nothing save some bats
which our entrance had disturbed and which broke the
solemn silence with the faint rustle of their velvety wings.

Children, and a good many grown-ups too, have an
instinctive urge to throw things down when they find
themselves on a hill-top or on the edge of a precipice or
on a bridge; no satisfactory explanation seems to have been
given for this involuntary reaction. The entire disappearance of loose stones from the immediate approaches
to certain well-known chasms and pot-holes is clear evidence
of the strength of such an urge. For ages, shepherds,
hunters, and walkers have picked up any stray object
which could be hurled into the depths, apparently for the
mere pleasure of waking the echoes and listening for the
crash of the falling body, the first impact the loudest, then
the sounds getting fainter and fainter as it penetrates the
mysterious darkness below.

Our Pont du Diable was strewn with rocks that had
fallen from above; obviously no one could have been here
before. So, partly in deference to a time-honoured custom,
partly with the object of finding out the depth of the abyss,
we heaved over one of the rocks. It plunged down,
bounded from the side with a thunderous crash and then,
a few seconds later, dived with a smack into deep water,
and finally the sheaf of water thrown up by the violent
disturbance fell back with the majestic but sinister sound
which is the knell of all that is engulfed beyond recall.

I uncoiled the rope and let it down, while my nimble
companion tied the other end neatly round a rocky spike,
securing it with a truly Gordian knot.

ON THE 'PONT DU DIABLE'

But before descending we thought it best to finish our exploration at our present level, for it extended almost horizontally in a glacis sloping very slightly towards the great pit. On the far side of this slope where we kicked off clods of earth into the pit, the cave opens out into a wide gallery. We strode rapidly across it till we came to a sudden step up in it which slightly overhung. The indispensable manœuvre of the *courte échelle* was successfully carried out. The sudden change to a higher level was followed by a narrowing tunnel, and we were very soon brought up in a cul-de-sac. A chimney, as wide as a man's body, offered a continuation upwards, but this too was blocked six feet up by a plug of stones solidly wedged together.

I drew Delteil's attention to some small snail shells and bits of vegetable refuse on the floor of the cave, which proved that the chimney must communicate with the surface of the ground, but how could any one say what depth of rock separated us from it?

While I was examining and gathering up these shells, my partner, despite my strict injunctions not to touch the stones, had not been able to keep his hands off them. Trying to clear a chimney from below is obviously a very risky business, and I was very quickly proved right by the collapse of a mass of rubble which poured down and rolled to my feet, leaving the marks of its passage on its rash disturber. Something like a cubic metre of stones had come away directly Delteil had tried to loosen it. He jumped back, but only the helmet I had given him to wear saved him from serious injury; as it was he got off with a few bruises and a slight shock; the helmet had some dents in it and the torch carried in front would not work.

'Too effective a job,' I commented, and followed by my climbing boy I left this evil chimney which was threatening a fresh avalanche, and went back to the rock bridge, where the smooth rope was inviting us to try a new sort of activity where there were other surprises in store for us; this cave is full of them.

This time it was a pleasant surprise, for, below the bridge, after the bare gloom of the great chamber and the avalanche in the chimney, there awaited us one of the unusual sights which give such attraction and charm to these explorations, and make us forget the times of weariness and danger we go through on expeditions that are toilsome and hazardous.

In a setting of spotless incrustations of white rock and great clusters of columns and stalactites, whose reflections met them as they plunged into its limpid surface, lay an underground lakelet, stretching away into dark mysterious little bays. Its waters appeared to reflect the roof with its masses of crystals, but this was an illusion; so perfectly clear was the water that at a depth of thirteen feet it was easy to see the delicate crystalline formations which made a carpet on the bottom in the way that corals do. Despite its absolute purity, the great depth of the water gave it an exquisite sea-green shade, for this is the true colour of pure water if it is sufficiently deep; just as the colour of air when it is pure and the light comes through a very deep layer of it, gives an azure tint to the sky. A band of white made a kind of shore along which fragile *gours* rose from below, their gadrooned edges just showing above the water, like braidings of white velvet. Where each white pillar met the surface of the lake it had formed a broad ring, white as the column above, floating like a water-lily. It is produced by the gradual accumulation of crystalline dust known as floating calcite which is sprinkled over the surface of some subterranean waters. But it was time to tear ourselves away from this fairyland, this scene from the *Arabian Nights*, for time was passing and other stretches of the cave lay in front of us.

By one of those contrasts peculiar to the underground world, which it would be a great mistake to fancy a dull world lacking in variety, our next advance took us through an appallingly muddy lobby, a veritable sewer of sticky clay in which we could hardly stand up, which clutched our legs and held them as if suckers had got hold of us. No bog on the surface can convey any idea of these underground sloughs, which have, however, this redeeming feature, that their mud is clean mud, if any mud can be called clean. It is a compound of clay and water, rather like the mixture worked up in making tiles and pottery. As there is no organic matter in it, no dung, it does not putrefy or smell, it is sterilized mud.

The helmet-topped figure floundering towards me in its blue overall, with its bulging rucksack and kit-bag, called up a vivid picture of an infantry relief in the muddy trenches of the last war.

Yet it is here in this lobby where it is hard to stagger along at all, with the loud clack of the sucking mud in our ears, that we had the most dramatic surprise of the day. Suddenly, above the sound of our sliding and stamping I detected a dull distant rumble which no spelaeologist could mistake. Hurrying on ahead, while my partner had not yet noticed it and had halted to deal with some difficulty or other, with his torch or equipment, I heard the characteristic roar of a waterfall becoming clearer. Louder and louder grew the noise till a turn in the direction of the cave brought me out of the muddy tunnel to a place overhanging a river, which plunged down in a huge cataract, just below where I stood, into a hole whose bottom was invisible. This meant that I had now got back to the same river that had stopped me at a siphon the previous day; my deductions as to the geological history of the place had enabled me to discover and use the earlier watercourse above and so circumvent the siphon.

At the present day the water has left the picturesque upper stages of the cave which we had traversed, and dashes down into the lower tunnel through the shaft of the waterfall now roaring past the spot on which I stood. The thrill of an important and decisive find of this kind comes as much from the inward satisfaction of having carefully constructed a theory and proved it right, as from the prospect of future further exploration which it affords. Above the fall I found the river flowing at a torrential speed through a tunnel with a lofty roof, an indication that there was no siphon beyond.

So the exploration of this underground river of Labouiche was about to enter on a new phase, and my thoughts naturally went back to the earlier explorers, of whom Martel was the first. I pictured the delight of this genuine expert (who, since he gave himself heart and soul to the task, never suffered from jealousy) if he could have known that this river, which he had always suspected of having a long course underground, had in fact a long history.

Delteil rejoined me at last, hobbling along, for in the mud he had lost one of the small anti-skid chains he had fastened to his boots. This accounted for his late arrival out of breath. But the moment he reached my level, he unrolled a spare rope he carried slung round him and I fixed it to a knob of rock in order to let myself down to the river. I landed just on the upper edge of the fall. A short distance down-stream the water becomes calm again, being held back by the obstruction of the siphon we had looked at the previous day, but there was no immediate possibility of descending to the foot of the fall, for the rope was not long enough.

Turning up-stream, I had to enter the water before I could climb two or three small waterfalls and cross a similar number of deep troughs; beyond these was a seemingly endless stretch of the river flowing in a rocky gallery, high and bare and waterworn.

The huge round holes, sharp sword-blades of rock, and smooth rounded stones showed that the river becomes a raging torrent in periods of heavy rain. As it was, a fairly prolonged drought enabled me to get along with only half my body under water. Even so, I had to pick my way carefully to avoid any deep places, for it was essential to avoid wetting the dry battery hung round my

AN UNDERGROUND LAKE

'GOURS' ON THE FLOOR OF A CAVE

neck, which supplied the electric bulb in my helmet.   I
left Delteil on the clay terrace, in charge of a less fragile
and precarious source of illumination, which allowed him
to await my return with an easy mind.   It would have
been too great a risk for both of us to enter the water.

My own anxiety as I pushed on quickly was not to
stumble and to keep an eye on the roof; it remained high
above me, and was therefore not likely for some time to
confront us with a siphon, that nightmare of cave explorers
which so often puts an end to their prospecting.   I had
progressed a further five hundred yards when the water
suddenly deepened and forced me to stop and put off any
further exploration till I could bring a more dependable
form of light and the rubber boat.   Before turning back I
had the satisfaction of seeing that the extension of the cave
looked as spacious as ever, and was almost straight.

Our journey back was, as you can well imagine, a toilsome business and the fatigue of the previous long struggle
made some of it extremely trying, but we were carrying
away a fine harvest of unforgettable scenes and our spirits
found unfailing sustenance in the prospect of soon returning
to resume this enthralling voyage of discovery.

Nor did we have to wait long for the realization of our
hopes.   Only a few days later, the rubber boat, duly
deflated and folded, was conveyed along the complicated
route described above and finally floated on the virgin
waters of the river.   But our cruise in it was not a long
one; a hundred yards beyond the limit of my previous
exploration an impenetrable siphon barred the way.

Shall we one day return to explore the ceiling of the
upper watercourse, hoping to find once more a storey above
by which to get past the new siphon?   Or, shall we leave
this cave and turn to others on our list and, if so, will
another thirty years elapse before our successors come along
to complete our work?

That is one more secret in the keeping of this cave of
Labouiche, with its strange and splendid river, where
c

tourists will soon be able to sail along at their ease, perhaps letting their minds dwell for a moment on the difficulties that faced the explorers, who, at the beginning of the century, first ventured into this wonder of the underground world.

2

THE POT-HOLES OF THE BASQUE COUNTRY

Now be stout and bold!
Now by such stairs must we descend.
DANTE, *Inferno*, canto xvii.

'Though I have visited a great number of canyons, underground rivers, caves, and pot-holes both in France and other countries, I can say without any hesitation that nowhere else have I seen anything like them, nor could the most vivid imagination conceive anything more fantastic, more awe-inspiring, and at the same time more entrancing.'

This is how the famous geologist and explorer Martel describes the gorges and pot-holes of the Basque country; his verdict is sufficient to establish the claims of the district to be a paradise for spelaeologists.

It was at the beginning of this century that Martel carried out some bold preliminary work in the very typical district of La Soule, one of the seven Basque provinces. He made a comprehensive list of these deep pot-holes, hidden away in mysterious mountain solitudes and gloomy forests, and had the courage to venture into some of these underground abysses.

He was stopped by the inadequacy of the equipment then in use and by the lack of assistance from his porters, whose efforts were paralysed by local superstitions, and also by the tremendous depth of the pot-holes; nevertheless he bravely unrolled his rope ladders and was let down into them.

Terrible avalanches of stones, loosened by the friction of his apparatus against the sides, forced him to retreat and give up any attempt at a thorough exploration of this dangerous Basque underworld.

27

Nevertheless, Martel's campaigns produced a mass of interesting information and unexpected discoveries, and drew attention to a district previously unknown.

It was not till twenty-five years later that a fresh party of explorers came to make a successful attack on these pot-holes. And a fine party they were: Max Cosyns and Vander Elst, the rivals of Professor Picard, the heroes of the first ascents into the stratosphere.

These two young Belgian experts, already quite at home in one domain hitherto unvisited and supposed to be inaccessible to man, had completely fallen in love with these abysses below the surface, the particular object of their attention being this bit of France which had given them a warm welcome in the 1914–18 war when they were still children.

From the start they attacked the deepest holes identified by Martel, the problems whose solution demanded the most strenuous efforts in fighting the opposition of rocks and water; such as the finding of the source and the exploration of the fine cascade which bursts out of the face of the cliffs in the gorge of Cacouette; it presents us with one of the most interesting water-puzzles in the Pyrenees. The two explorers, with the help of their friend Pécher, reached the point where the cascade issues from the cliff by a novel and successful manœuvre such as one might expect from men who were utterly unaffected by giddiness. They made a vertical descent of nearly eight hundred feet down the face of the cliff which overhangs the gorge, tied by a belt to a thin steel rope.

They did a great deal of exploratory work in caves, on underground rivers, and in pot-holes; in one case, in July 1935, making a new record in depth for French spelaeology.

It was about that time that the kind idea occurred to Max Cosyns of asking me to collaborate with him in his most attractive pioneering work. For the moment I could not accept his invitation as I had damaged myself going down a pot-hole, but I was able to join him the following year.

Our first meeting took place in the charming village of Licq at the Hôtel des Touristes, the very spot where Martel, who had put us in communication with one another, often stayed when he was himself working in the district.

There in a bedroom, transformed into a storeroom of apparatus, I made acquaintance with the amazing devices used by my new colleagues. Only a few years before I had had my first great surprise on seeing the equipment so well thought out and adapted for use by my friend de Joly, the president of the Société Spéléologique de France, which has given new life to the art of pot-holing. But now I stood in dumb astonishment as I looked at extraordinary contrivances, which seemed to be the combined products of a physical laboratory, an arms factory, and a diver's wardrobe.

One after the other I was shown, among other objects whose use I could only guess at, accurately recording aeronautical instruments for use underground, a machine-gun tripod of duralumin, apparently used as the base of a portable windlass, a sort of miniature machine-gun used as a pistol for piercing holes in very hard rock in order to insert pitons, strait-waistcoats which were really parachutists' harness, and strange suits of rubber clothing for exploring underground streams. Of knotted ropes, or of rope ladders, not a sign! Not a yard of them! I was told, and I was almost ready to believe, that these deserters from the stratosphere were in the habit of descending pot-holes by parachute!

The night before my first exploration with my new friends was one of dreadful dreams, in which ascents into the stratosphere alternated with falls into nightmare abysses.

Next day the party, consisting of Max Cosyns and his wife, Vander Elst, and myself, with two porters and a mule, went up into the canyon district. A long climb through the forest brought us, at a height of four thousand five hundred feet, to the pot-hole of Utciapia, one of the deepest in the Basque country.

The week before, my companions had gone down this shaft, but had been unable to reach the bottom and were now returning to the attack, a common sequel to attempts of this kind.

With the help of the two porters (one of whom was a son of Arnaud Bouchet who had been Martel's guide in this region) my friends proceeded to set up the tripod which had puzzled me the day before. A light bracket of steel tubing with a grooved pulley at the end was fixed to the frame of the windlass, so that it projected over the pot-hole. A heavy spool of thin steel cable was placed behind it on a support, the end of the cable was carried round the cylindrical drum of the windlass and then fitted into the groove of the pulley.

All was now ready for the descent, for in the meantime I had got into my parachutist's harness; it felt heavy and cumbrous, but is said to be reasonably comfortable for descents made hanging in mid air. A small telephone attached to my chest and my helmet with its frontal torch completed my equipment. In necessary observance of the rules of courtesy, my friends had offered me the place of honour. As I knew nothing about the working of the windlass or the methods of my friends, it was only natural to trust myself entirely to them and let myself be dropped first to the bottom of the hole. Only natural, I admit; but what appeared a less simple matter was to trust myself to that thin steel cable, whose end was there dangling in the jaws of the pot-hole, as if it invited me to come and do the same, like a puppet on a string!

I took the greatest interest in all the preparations and in learning how the windlass worked; it had an arrangement for changing gear, a brake, and a safety clutch. But it was the wire rope that interested me most at the moment and I gazed at it with a suspicious eye. The cable, I was told—and cable seemed rather a big name for it—was made of a certain number of galvanized steel threads specially treated and drawn. But what I remember to have struck me most about it when I looked at it and thought about it was its thickness, which was only one-fifth of an inch.

The expression 'hanging by a thread' had never appeared to me more appropriate and more unpleasing than when, with the ring at the end of the wire rope linked into the clasp-ring of my harness, I deliberately took the step forward which left me hanging in mid-air, while the metal windlass looked to me deplorably frail and pliable as it bent and creaked under the strain.

Everything being ready our two helpers began to work the handles of the windlass and my descent began to the rattling accompaniment of the pawl in the ratchet. As my eyes came level with the rim of the pot-hole the vision of this peaceful bit of forest was suddenly replaced by the familiar but always impressive sight of a gaping chasm with damp glistening walls hung with hart's-tongue and soft wads of moss, with knobs of rock protruding over the abyss like gargoyles.

A sudden stoppage in my descent followed by a re-ascent accompanied by sundry exclamations gave me rather a shock; however, it was nothing serious, merely that I had forgotten the 'spider.' The spider is a small pulley mounted on a claw-shaped trivet, which I was supposed to fix in the wall of the pot-hole where a protruding rock caused an overhang a few yards below.

After groping about for a little I managed to fix the thing right under the windlass; then, having fitted the rope that held me into the groove of the pulley so as to avoid wear and tear by friction against the rocks, I continued my descent.

Below the overhang the hole widens out considerably and I went down out of reach of the walls, dropping in space. Nor was it long before I began to be conscious of the drawbacks of my position, for a gyratory movement began which soon developed into a wider and faster swing. In the almost complete darkness the feeble beam of my torch could only catch a few details of the cyclopean walls, and before long the movement became so violent that my eyes failed to register any impression at all.   As I passively turned round and round, certain bits of Martel's description of this pot-hole kept passing through my mind: 'The tremendous falls of loose bits of rock and the rotten nature of the sides prohibited any descent below a hundred and thirty feet.   It would mean death under avalanches of falling stones.'

What depth, I wondered, had I actually reached?   At any rate, in spite of the horrid gyrations and the fears the thinness of the rope aroused in me, I had to admit that not a single stone had come down the shaft, a result of the excellent technique of the Belgian spelaeologists and a very adequate compensation for any gyratory movement, however unpleasant.   The places where the friction of the ladders against the disintegrating surface of the walls had brought down avalanches of rocks and made a further descent impossible for Martel were passed in silence without any contact with the sides as I hung suspended in the middle of the vast pit.

Only one point of contact existed, where the spider pulley was fixed to its rocky bracket; the slight creak it made in turning grew fainter and fainter and it kept the wire rope well away from the death-dealing walls.   While noting the superiority of this way of doing things, I was conscious of a horrid feeling inside akin to seasickness.

Not till that moment had I thought of the telephone at my chest.   Pressing the button I sent up a call to the surface and a conversation began along the steel cable, which acted as a conveyer of messages besides taking my weight.   All these improvements helped to reconcile me to the said cable.   I was asked if I was turning at all, to which I replied: 'Quite a lot and jolly fast.'   The voice from above assured me there was not much more to come and that I should soon be touching the bottom or at any rate a first big ledge, below which the shaft goes down into still unexplored depths. My giddily rotating descent continued like a dive into the bowels of the earth till, all of a sudden, I had a vague impression of a debris slope and my feet came with a rude shock against a pile of scree and dead branches.

The sudden contact with the sloping ground and the tangle of wood made me lose my balance; in addition the heavy harness and other equipment weighed me down and I fell on my knees. So I telephoned as quickly as I could to stop the unrolling of the windlass as I was being tied up in coils of steel cable.

This was the first relay point, where I was to take off my harness, untie myself from the cable, and wait for another of the party to join me.

My first act was to unhook from my belt my faithful acetylene lamp, light it, and let it give me a glimpse of the great shaft I had descended practically blindfold. Far above me I could just make out the faint diffused light of the sky, filtering through the forest foliage.

From where I stood a steep slope of loose scree plunged down out of sight into the gaping jaws of a lower chasm into which we meant to try to descend that day.

While having my look round I had got rid of my harness, leaving it attached to the end of the cable, and I telephoned that they could begin hauling it up. Before doing so, Cosyns informed me with his usual accuracy that I was at that moment four hundred and ten feet below the surface, a fact which explained the time I had taken to come down and the amplitude of the gyratory movement. Professor Barbican, the hero of *Voyage de la terre à la lune*, would have found here ready to hand the famous vertical cannon he had cast in an artificial pit nine hundred feet deep.

I sat on the scree slope and looked up the enormous tube, quite thirty feet wide and absolutely vertical, and I reflected that my harness, as it went up without my weight to keep the swing in check, might at any moment loosen bits of rock from the walls or knock off stones lying on narrow ledges.

Now in a pot-hole as deep as this, the smallest missiles attain a high speed and striking force. So I took the precaution of crouching against the side with my Tyrolean rucksack on my knees and my head protected by my helmet and a coil of rope ladder which I had brought down in case of emergency; a simple precaution, but by no means a useless one, for presently disturbing sounds began to reach me.

Far up the shaft I heard the sounds of something ricocheting against the walls, to be followed by the horrible whinings getting louder and louder which herald and accompany the arrival of shells, those rushing blasts which no old soldier will ever forget. The rattle of this discharge of missiles was amplified by the acoustic properties of the shaft as it bore down upon the poor human grub below and hit the slope with terrifying violence and momentum.

I was unhurt, the only damage being to the aluminium reflector of my lamp which was flattened as it lay beside me. A sudden reaction to the danger made me jump up, and catching sight of a narrow recess a few yards above me in the wall, I tried to climb up into it, while a few of the stones which had rolled down the slope were still rebounding from side to side of the shaft below. It was like an upper window, very narrow and difficult to reach, the holds being small, but the fear of being bombarded again brought out all my resources as a climber. I managed to raise myself to the level of the opening, slipped hurriedly through it, and to my astonishment found myself in a recess like a miniature grotto, where I could sit down and recover my equanimity. After my spell of acrobatics on an exposed wall and the alarming cannonade, I had found a safe haven in this delightful little cave suitable for gnomes, where my eye lighted with affection on some clusters of slender translucent stalactites and embossed draperies on the walls, which bore witness, even at this great depth and close to the horrible bare, avalanche-swept shaft, to the slow, graceful work of water, falling drop by drop. It is often so underground; chaos in all its primitive savagery, the most frightful convulsions of nature, are found side by side with scenes that have all the charm of fairyland.

Knowing from experience how long these manœuvres with ropes can take in pot-holing I settled down for a stay in my lonely retreat. I propped myself up, with my lamp between my knees, and endeavoured with the help of a couple of stones to mend my reflector, which had been hemispherical and was now flattened. Memories of the classics brought a smile to my lips: Vulcan forging thunder-bolts for Jove or the weapons of Cupid in the subterranean dwellings of the Cyclops! But while I was hammering away on my prehistoric anvil of stone, sounds of a fresh tornado came from the shaft. Another avalanche of stones crashed down on the slope I had just quitted. I enjoyed that rare and personal satisfaction of danger passing close at hand and knowing that whatever happens one is safe oneself.

My rough repairs to the reflector had been so successful that it now shed a fine light on the various details of the cave. In one recess, where a projecting ledge had been hollowed out like a stoup, I caught the glitter of a small basin of water of the crystal clearness only seen under-ground. The bottom of the basin was starred with crystalline fronds of a structure as delicate as that of coral, an enchanting submarine landscape in miniature. The tiny ocean had a shore of fine ooze, on which some active little creatures were running about in all directions. Something had alarmed these minute amber-coloured, almost transparent beetles, causing them to dash about on the edge of the pond which was their home, though they knew neither its outline nor its colour, being not merely blind but entirely without organs of sight, which would be perfectly useless to them in the complete darkness of the great pit.

These cave-dwelling insects, perhaps unknown and a consequent source of delight to an entomologist who could saddle them with some Latin or Greek name, possess highly developed senses which make up for their lack of sight and which gave them all the necessary information about my arrival, an event entirely without precedent in their mysterious existence. They hurried off into narrow fissures to find there, in peace, the unending night in which it is their destiny to live. And a strange destiny it is for these insects, who will never know the blessedness of light and the warm rays of the sun, or the countless intoxicating scents among which their brethren on the surface live and frolic. Poor wee creatures, whose brief life is spent far from the rest of the world, in entire ignorance of what is indispensable to us, the blue sky, the good earth, the sun, the alternations of night and day and of the seasons, trees, flowers, in fact, life itself. It may be, after all, that for these creatures who seem to have no share in our heritage, there are compensations of which we have no idea. Moreover, this darkness and isolation in which they live, dreadful as it must seem to us, is undoubtedly for them the only possible way of life, the most peaceful, that which agrees best with the conception of happiness expressed in the saying: 'Pour vivre heureux, vivons cachés.'

While my thoughts were wandering off and groping their way into distant dark ages when this diminutive race of cave-dwellers came to take up their abode underground and my mind was getting lost in philosophical speculations, a strange yell jerked me out of my reverie. It came from friend Cosyns hanging on his steel thread, who was waking up again the echoes of the shaft and was possibly wondering at my silence. I stuck my nose out of my rock window and replied with a resounding yell, trying at the same time to make out the outline of the figure that must be swinging round up there in space instead of me.

Suddenly a succession of flashes struck through the darkness and a bright pencil of light, thin and long like that from a lighthouse, swept down along the wall till it came to the scree slope.   It was the electric torch with variable focus, the latest gadget science has bestowed on the spelaeologist; it definitely dispelled my previous doubts as to the use of electricity underground.   These high-power lamps are really marvellous; with them you can pierce the darkness at over three hundred feet, a priceless boon, especially in vertical shafts where ordinary lamps are not effective beyond sixty feet.   I took advantage of the light moving along the walls of the shaft to study their structure; it was actually what I had imagined it to be from the glimpses I had had, just a gigantic cannon pointed towards the zenith.

The light came nearer and nearer; there were even attempts at conversation, but the echoes which the inter-fering waves of sound produced made the words unin-telligible.

At more than thirty or forty yards it is impossible to talk or make any vocal communication in these holes; hence the necessity of the telephone.

All at once I had to draw my head back quickly into my niche as the warning of a new rain of missiles reached me.   Oddly enough I could not hear them whistling, nor the noise as they struck the ground. . . . I peeped out and saw other dark points apparently suspended in the air and fluttering slowly down.   Could they be bats?   No, they were just beech leaves swept off by the men working up above and which now came twirling down on to the slope, making their contribution to the layer of rotting vegetation which has been accumulating for ages at the bottom of the shaft.

I waited a moment or two while silence was restored, then I began to make out the form of Max Cosyns twirling round just like a leaf.   The sight of him hanging like that, his nailed boots swinging in circles and looking grotesquely large owing to foreshortening, made me think of this same man on a very different occasion, soaring at ten miles above the earth in the upper reaches of the atmosphere, in a zone which none had ever entered before, regarded as inaccessible, where the temperature sinks to sixty degrees below zero and the human body would burst if exposed outside the air-tight nacelle.

I am sure he was as cool and collected then as he appeared to be now as he came down. He landed, took off his harness, asked what I thought of the place, and began a conversation on the telephone with the windlass team.

Our plans for immediate exploration were fixed up. The descents and ascents, to say nothing of minor operations involved, took so long that Vander Elst decided not to come down, but to stay with the windlass; it was clearly of vital importance that it should be carefully and wisely used. Mme Cosyns was to attend to the telephone while we carried our explorations further down. The scree-slope at this first landing point was cluttered up, especially at its upper end, with trunks and branches of trees, which greatly hampered our movements and the free use of our appliances, and it was also a surprise to us to find that communication with the lower continuation of the shaft was by a crevice only just wide enough to crawl through. So narrow was it that we gave up the idea of descending by the wire cable, for with the harness on we should not have got through.

Accordingly my rope ladder was unwound and let down into the hole; the top of the ladder was hooked on to the ring at the end of the steel cable, and after Cosyns had telephoned up a warning to put the stop-catch on the windlass I forced myself through the narrow passage between the ladder and the wall.

Lower down the shaft becomes as vertical and of as ample proportions as above. It was time to look out for some stopping place, some projecting ledge where I could rest my feet and put on the harness when my friend had slipped it through the crevice I had just passed. Keeping a good hold of the ladder, I turned on the electric torch to see if there was some suitable abutment and also to try to estimate the depth of the new shaft. And there, some sixty feet down, the beam revealed a horizontal bit of ground, which looked as if it might well be the bottom of the hole. Projecting bulges of rock prevented my seeing the whole of the floor, so, to make quite sure, I climbed down the ladder till I got there. It was actually the bottom where the hole came to a sudden end. Standing in this pit five hundred feet deep, trodden for the first time by the foot of man, I let my partner know what it was like there. The damp floor was strewn with bits of rock and on it were three skulls of sheep, the deep black sockets of the eyes even after death suggesting the pathetic tragedy of their end. A gloomy thought indeed, this great pit with its mouth open for prey in the depths of the forest, drawing these poor beasts down its black throat far from the sheltering sheepfolds and the beds of bracken that belong to this good Basque country.

We returned to the surface in the same order as we came down, I myself being drawn up first, without any appreciable effort on my part, a very different sort of journey from that up a rope ladder from such a great depth, which always puts a tremendous strain upon the muscles and is quite the most violent and exhausting form of exercise I know. By the time Cosyns had been drawn up after me and all the apparatus taken to pieces and collected, night was falling and we went off to find shelter and roll ourselves in our rugs in the *cayolar* of Utciapia, a shepherd's hut erected in a clearing near by.

Our small party was already on the move again at daybreak; Mme Cosyns with the porters and the mule went down to the valley, while Max Cosyns, Vander Elst, and I went up over the mountains, with bulky sacks on our backs, to search for pot-holes in the neighbourhood of the frontier.

The ascent through the forest was tedious, as the first stage of a climb generally is; no vista broke its green monotony, for until we had got above the wooded zone any extensive view of the country was impossible. When we did emerge from it, we saw the chain of the Pyrenees stretching away on either side of us, from the Pic d'Anie and the Pic d'Arlas in the east to the Pic d'Orrhy and La Rhune which rises from the shore of the Atlantic. The plains of France remained hidden under a splendid sea of cloud.

We went on over vast stretches of barren hillside, we dipped into valleys, climbed over great buttresses, making steadily for the frontier ridge. About midday, after marking the position of several holes at the head of the canyon of Uhadjarré, we lunched in the Val d'Eruso and then began a fresh ascent to a region of boulders and deep holes. Our intention was to descend from there by following the top of the cliffs of the famous canyon of Cacouette and rejoin our porters who were to meet us at the opening of the great pot-hole of Heyle. The morning mists, which had at first been low and localized, had risen higher and higher during the day and were now rolling forward at our level. Quite suddenly, as is apt to happen in the mountains, we found ourselves in dense fog just as we were nearing the frontier ridge. Visibility was limited to a few yards, and every landmark had vanished. For all we knew, we might already be in Spanish territory, a thing to be avoided, seeing that the country was far from safe; at that moment fierce fighting was going on in the adjoining district of Irun.

Luckily for us, Cosyns had his compass with him, enabling him to steer us in the right direction, so that by the end of the day we actually found ourselves in the middle of the forest of Heyle, at the edge of the pot-hole that bears its name.

The opening, about two hundred feet by one hundred feet, is a most impressive sight. It is a great natural portal

AN UNDERGROUND LAKELET

A NEW STRETCH OF THE RIVER

of five separate arches. A luxuriant carpet of vegetation covers all this bit of the forest, and it is especially thick at the brink of the abyss, which is constantly emitting puffs of cold, damp air; as a result a plume of white mist often marks this grand and awe-inspiring entrance.

The depth of this pot-hole, the second deepest in France, its forbidding appearance, and the lavish way it showers down stones had frightened away the few explorers who had come to plumb its shaft. In 1935 Cosyns and Vander Elst had set up their windlass on the edge of the hole and had ventured down into this 'thunder-pit,' reaching the great depth of eight hundred feet. Now our party had met round the orifice with the intention of descending even further into the interior of the mountain to try to track down the mysterious watercourse which feeds the cascade of Cacouette and bursts out of the face of the cliff in the neighbouring canyon.

When the porters arrived it was too late to make any attempt that day; so we merely unloaded the mule, cached our apparatus in the bushes, and retired, putting off our exploration till the morning. However, before leaving, we did our best to divert the course of a stream which disappeared a hundred yards away from the pot-hole into a narrow hole in the rock discovered by Vander Elst. Through this vertical shaft, no wider than a man's body, there came a current of cold air which blew about the grass round it; there was evidently a possibility it was connected with the great pot-hole near it.

Next day, owing to a break in the weather, we arrived late at the scene of action. While Vander Elst and the porters were busy preparing the descent into the Heyle pit, Cosyns and I carried out an exploration of the blow-hole by means of my rope ladders.

The small cascade which still fell into it, spreading out as it fell, was a very unpleasant hindrance. Both of us went down nearly a hundred and twenty feet, then I went on to the bottom, which I came to at two hundred and forty

D

feet.   The descent was complicated by the extreme narrowness of the shaft at certain points and by a loose slab of
rock, which was moved out of place by the friction of the
ladder and blocked the passage above me, besides threatening to fall and crush me if disturbed in any way. . . .
However, I succeeded in escaping from this awkward
predicament, and when we came up again to the light of
day, we found it was raining almost as hard outside as in
the shaft.

For some days the weather had been explaining to us
the secret of the verdant aspect and luxuriant vegetation of
the Basque country; now the rain drove us down again.
Next day, though the rain had not stopped, it was less
heavy, and we found ourselves once more at the entrance
to the great pot-hole.   Cosyns had been unexpectedly
detained in the village, so it was Vander Elst who was to
come down with me, trusting to the stalwart arms of our
faithful allies, Sauveur Bouchet and Martin Haristoy.

For the reasons given above in the story of our exploration of the Utciapia hole, I was to descend first.   Before
I put on the harness, Vander Elst made me slip under my
linen overall a light waterproof garment cut out of the
actual cover of the balloon F.N.R.S. made for the stratosphere, which one day floated over most of Europe before
tearing itself to bits when it landed on some sharp rocks.
It was like a diver's costume, absolutely watertight, without
any opening, and was meant to be a protection against the
low temperature down in the hole.

And in fact, only a few yards down, I found myself
passing through a dense growth of bracken and moss
dripping with water.   Below this I had once more the
thrilling sensation of going down a vertical shaft in rock.
But in this case, owing to the structure of the walls, I was
not kept hanging isolated in mid air.   Every now and
then my hands and feet struck against the sides, checking
or avoiding any tendency to turn.   Consequently, I was
able to be let down without any unpleasant effects or dis-

comfort, swathed in rolls of rope and rope ladders in a way that would nullify the impact of any stones that might descend on me; these implements were to be our stand-by in the lower reaches of the hole, where the cable could not be used.

Five hundred feet below ground I landed on the usual boulder-covered slope, the rubbish-tip which was evidence of the vast mass of rocks, stones, and branches of trees engulfed in the course of ages. On the mouldy wood grew a close crop of the strangest-looking phosphorescent mushrooms.

Taught by recent experience I looked out for some cover from stone-falls, and crouching under an overhang I proceeded to light my acetylene lamp and telephone to the top that the harness could be pulled up, as I had taken it off.

The day's descent of five hundred feet at a single stretch was the longest I had yet made. I have actually reached much lower depths, as low as one thousand feet, but in several relays, none of which was as long as the one just effected.

My companion's arrival was, as I had foreseen, long delayed. Unless you have actual experience of them, you cannot imagine how slow, how full of small checks and difficulties these pot-holing operations can be.

Uncomfortably perched on the crumbling slope, as at the bottom of the Utciapia hole, but not so well under cover, I waited, looked about me, and listened; three occupations which often go together underground. I may mention that in some of these subterranean relaying performances spelaeologists have been known to watch and wait for fifteen hours on end, perched on ledges or narrow balconies overhanging space, fighting against cold, penetrating damp, and sleep!

Below where I stood the debris fanned out into the darkness. A bat, possibly disturbed by the noise of my descent, emerged from the gloom and flew up the shaft, ascending in gently rising spirals. What an immense depth these little creatures reach! I have met them in the very longest of my explorations, sometimes in huge caverns, miles away from the light of day.

From time to time stones came whistling down on to the slope, riddling the layers of decaying vegetation and releasing smells of cryptogamous growths.

There was also a heap of bones of animals among the debris, for this pot-hole of Heyle is a natural death-trap for anything that ventures near the brink of its funnel.

Fortunately on this occasion there was no recent victim, so I was spared the proximity of a rotting carcase, a quite common occurrence.

From the rocky chimney above came the sound of Vander Elst's musical young voice. As he descended he telephoned a message to the men at the windlass, then gave me a cheerful hail and was soon landed beside me, heavily laden like myself. It was now four o'clock. Everything being ready for proceeding with our exploration, we left the end of the cable here, as well as the telephone, after sending word to those above that we should not call them up before six o'clock. Then, carrying our stock of ropes and ladders, we plunged down the slope, at the bottom of which we came into a large level hall with a roof so high that its details were indistinguishable.

This vast and beautiful cavern was discovered by Vander Elst the year before, and he proceeded to point out its splendours. It suggested some fine underground cathedral, with all the columns and works of sculpture with which that imaginative worker the stalagmite has lavishly adorned it. The span of the roof is beyond anything possible to human architecture; the height is incredible. It was here that he and Cosyns, held enthralled by their discovery, decided to spend the night on the occasion of their first descent. Vander Elst showed me, as we passed it, the recess where they bivouacked and spent a good night in their sleeping-bags, deep in the bowels of the earth, despite the draughts and low temperature.

After inspecting this magnificent nave over five hundred and twenty feet long and noting a few details of scientific interest, we made our way over to the point where the cave descends again, in a sort of sloping passage room, till it is suddenly broken by a vertical drop. Here we uncoiled and fixed our rope ladders. In this case the use of the steel cables is rendered impracticable by the horizontal stretches and the changes of direction in the cave. Lowering by cable can only be employed in vertical descents immediately below the windlass.

Descending either by the rope ladder or by the smooth rope or by using the numerous rough holds for hands and feet on the walls themselves, we explored a whole maze of pits, galleries, and clefts till we came to the lowest point reached by Cosyns the year before, some eight hundred feet below the surface. Despite all our researches pursued into the narrowest of joints, into oubliettes, into drainpipes of the tightest fit, we found nothing new and could get no further than our predecessors, whose boots had left nailmarks everywhere on the soft rocks.

Leaving Vander Elst in the 'cathedral' to ensure telephonic communication with the men at the surface, this wonderful fellow Cosyns had examined all the lower parts of the chasm with an attention to detail and a nerve to which I take off my hat, for exploring alone at depths like this is no ordinary exploit.

Our own explorations had taken a long time, for when we had re-ascended the rope ladders, climbed the debris slope, and coiled up and piled our equipment beside the telephone at the top of it, it was already nine o'clock.

Conversation by telephone with the party above in the open was difficult, as the instrument sometimes failed to work; I can still hear Vander Elst's repeated calls, calm and persistent: 'Allô, Sauveur! Allô, Sauveur!' In that chilly darkness of the pit, five hundred feet underground, this litany, issuing in a steady stream from a figure kneeling in the mud over the telephone, was quite an impressive performance, and I could not help thinking there was a certain apt fatality about the name of the young Basque whom we were so fervently begging for an answer to our prayers.

At last the friendly voice reached us. The two Basques had waited crouching under a tree for hours and in considerable anxiety while the rain poured down. The faint tinkle of the telephone had ended their long vigil, but, having no light of any kind, they had had to be very careful in approaching the edge of the chasm. The news sent down by Sauveur was that it was as dark above as in the hole, a pitch-dark night.

One of the couplings of the windlass had got out of order, and in the dark it was impossible to see exactly what was wrong, but our two men evidently thought the machine was not working as it should. We had a suspicion they were hiding some serious mishap from us, for the porters asked if we would mind spending the night down below, so that they could pull us up next morning in the safest possible conditions. A short consultation had to do for a council of war. Being asked what should be done, I answered that I was not competent to make any decision about the windlass and cable, but that if it was thought best to spend the night at the bottom of the hole, I was quite willing.

There was certainly nothing in the prospect of such a night out to daunt my companion, though on this occasion there would be no sort of covering for us; I think it was the fear in his twenty-five-year-old stomach of having nothing to put in it for so long that made him decide to get back to the surface, whatever happened.

He put on the harness as though he expected an exciting time, for we knew something had gone wrong with the apparatus, telephoned that he was ready, and gave the signal to start. To our great relief he swung clear at the first pull and the upward movement seemed quite normal; but it did not last long. Barely thirty feet up the first sudden stoppage occurred, followed by a succession of jerks and a prolonged halt.

I wonder how many times such stoppages, with their accompanying shocks, were repeated on this memorable occasion. I was horribly anxious for my companion as he swung about in space at increasing heights, where the breaking of the cable must have been fatal; or, if not that, he might have been suspended without any possibility of rescue by the definite breakdown of the winding apparatus.

Not for a moment did he show the slightest sign of being worried, nor did he address a single question to the men above, who must have been having an awful time with the winding, coupled with the dread of not being able to get us up.

I am not going to indulge in a detailed description of a situation which suggested strangely unpleasant possibilities; I will say no more than that the fifty minutes of its duration seemed endless. Afterwards I asked Vander Elst what his impressions had been at the time, and he confided to me that he had been wondering from what height he would have to fall to be killed on the spot.

After enduring so much anxiety as to what might happen to my companion, I naturally felt some on my own account when my turn came. To begin with, the harness sent down again at the end of the cable only reached me after innumerable delays in manœuvring it off projections in the wall, on which the wretched thing would catch. Then came a repetition of the first ascent, a series of stoppages and jerks, with nasty quiverings and sudden tensions of the cable, which made me think every time it was going to break and let me fall. To add to all this, I had put on the harness clumsily in the darkness, the straps were hurting, and I felt as if I were being pulled to pieces by the weight of the ropes and ladders and other accessories with which I was laden. All the same, I was luckier than Vander Elst, for thanks to the aid of his stout arms at the windlass it took only twenty-five minutes to hoist me to ground-level.

Those twenty-five minutes gave me an opportunity of comparing the merits of a single cable and a rope ladder, and I must admit that the favourable impression I had recently formed of the cable in the pot-hole of Utciapia, gave place to a marked preference for the rope ladders I habitually used and which I regretted having ever abandoned.

Sauveur had not exaggerated, it was as dark in the open as in the lowest part of the hole. By the light of our electric torches we stumbled about in the heavy, sopping bracken among bits of apparatus strewn all over the place.

It was no time for explanations about the defective working of the windlass. We hastily piled as many packages as we could on our backs, leaving the rest to be fetched later, and set off, having almost to feel our way forward.

Walking, even in this vague stumbling fashion, soon induced in us the sort of rhythmic motion familiar to climbers, which enables them to keep going mechanically and apparently without effort, even at the end of a long day. Animal spirits are restored by reaction after hours of stress and help to buck one up, however weary one may be and craving to be fed. Giving outward expression to this relaxation of strain, one of the porters suddenly straightened himself to his full height and made the darkness quiver with a wild *irrintzina*. This shrill, long-drawn-out cry, believed to be the war-cry of the mountaineers of old, went echoing through the gorge of Cacouette near by. As we listened to the echoes getting fainter and fainter, another cry rang out from the middle of the forest followed by a succession of neighs. Our two porters, galvanized into a frenzy of enthusiasm by this response, began to exchange with this mysterious partner a series of indescribable howls, hoarse mewings, guttural yells, and hyena's laughter which it was hard to believe could come from human throats. Long ago

Roland and his paladins must have heard these terrifying *irrintzinas* in the neighbouring valley of Roncevaux. Without any doubt, these howlings were originally intended to impress the enemy, as they certainly can astonish any one who hears them for the first time at night in the still solitudes of the mountains.

The vocal contest came to an end at last and Sauveur informed us he had recognized the voice of one of his brothers. Presumably he was with a search party coming to look for us, for it was after midnight. We met it, in fact, a few minutes later on the path. It consisted of Max Cosyns and a brother of Bouchet's, both quite out of breath, for they had climbed at a great pace. Not seeing us at the time arranged Cosyns had set off with a companion, fearing an accident had occurred.

We all went down through the forest of Heyle singing as we went, to the gorge of Saint-Engrâce, where a car was waiting, which brought us back to the village at two o'clock in the morning overcome with sleep. At the Hôtel Bouchet we found the warmest of welcomes and good food awaiting us. They had all been anxious about us and some of the guests we knew had not gone to bed, but waited to see us come in.

In concluding this description of my two or three explorations of pot-holes, I must point out that I have confined myself to certain incidents and have given a very incomplete and fragmentary account of the enormous amount of work carried out by my Belgian friends. The most important omission is that of the scientific results of their investigations of these caves of the Basque Pyrenees; these results are remarkable, but are too technical to be dealt with in these pages. Some brief allusion to them is, I think, permissible, if only to explain the persistence shown in some of these researches and the fatigue and risks involved in prospecting far underground. Such dangerous explorations might be justified by a comparison with mountaineering, where climbers seem to look for what is difficult and dangerous, preferring out-of-the-way routes beset with risks to those recognized as the simplest.

But the lure of danger, the satisfaction of overcoming difficulties and of dominating fear, is only one aspect, a mere incident, of exploration underground. For such explorations open up fascinating subjects for research too numerous to mention here. They invite us, for example, to study and make philosophical speculations about the prehistoric life or the biological significance of creatures we know little of, and then perhaps draw us on to questions of hydrogeology and the mysterious problems of radiation and even of cosmic rays which still await solution.

Finally, underlying all, to use an appropriate phrase, there is a primitive novelty about the surroundings in which these explorations are carried out; the things we see have the charm of what is strange as well as grand; it is a world for poets, this realm underground, where wonderful processes carry on the work of nature in a never-ending night, in a solitude such as the world above has never known.

3

CRAWLING DOES IT

Where there's a will, there's a way.

C. HUDSON.

On land, on water, and in the air, man has succeeded in taming the elements one after another, in making them the servants of his genius, of his lust for conquest and material progress.

Having done his running and leaping with the means his own body supplied, and then bringing to his aid all manner of things to ride on and to drive in, he has not only succeeded in matching in speed the fleetest of animals, but thanks to modern methods of locomotion has far surpassed anything known in the animal world.

Having begun by swimming, then steered his way over the water in frail, easily upset boats propelled by arm-power, he has now learned to drive through the seas, first in sailing boats, now in fast powerful ships; he has even succeeded in burrowing beneath the waves in the diving-bell, in the diver's dress, in the submarine, and the bathysphere.

In the air, the domain which he has taken so long to conquer, man's genius has at last managed to emancipate him from the terrible law of gravity, which seemed to defy all his efforts, and it is in this element of the air that he has attained the dizziest speeds and has displayed the most astonishing skill and the most incredible audacity, enjoying at heights that reach the stratosphere the most intoxicating forms of peril.

Rolling along, sailing or flying at increasing speeds over all the roads and oceans of the globe or in its air, is there any conquest left to tempt the ambition of the human race?

Is there yet one more element to be conquered, a realm to bring into service, a new method of locomotion to be used? Yes, is our answer. Man has still to penetrate the terrestrial globe and move about inside it; as yet, we only occupy and know its outer surface.

No doubt, thanks to the *conquête minérale*, the epic achievement described by that great geologist Louis de Launay, we already have mines, tunnels, and deep shafts which penetrate the ground in places; but the outer skin of the earth's crust concerned in these pioneering works is so insignificant compared with the vast mass of our planet that such undertakings can only be regarded as the tiniest pin-pricks.

If we consider the great advances in other domains of nature, is it so very impossible and senseless to visualize a method of penetration and locomotion underground that would be comparatively rapid, a sort of engine provided with powerful cutting and boring tools in which it would be possible to move through the interior of the earth, carrying out quite long journeys beneath the surface down to depths hitherto undreamt of? It may be that the realization of this idea will not come about till we can travel from this planet to others—another bold anticipation of events, but one whose *theoretical* possibility has been already studied and determined.

I see no reason why a deep penetration of this old earth of ours should offer a harder problem than that involved in lifting ourselves into the air. That 'heavier than air' problem, like that of perpetual motion and the squaring of the circle, was considered a Utopian aspiration; yet it was just when most learned scientific conferences were solemnly recording the absurdity of this chimerical idea that the first flying machine was leaving the ground.

Possibly the reason we are behindhand with our underground prospecting is simply that the need for it has not yet become imperative. That day will assuredly come, and perhaps sooner than we think. Geologists have already calculated the date when we can expect our reserves of coal and oil to be exhausted; and already new and improved methods of prospecting are in operation to sound the earth's crust and reveal the riches it conceals. The aim of geophysics, a science born less than fifty years ago, is to explore what is below the surface, basing its conclusions on the measurements of certain physical properties of the strata. Various experimental methods, magnetic, gravimetric, seismographic, had already given interesting indications; but an amazing discovery, of which too little is known, made by the French expert Conrad Schlumberger (who died still young in 1936), enabled geophysics to make an immense stride forward. A method of prospecting, based on the electrical resistance of rocks, is now giving astonishing results. The precise nature of what lies at very great depths below the surface can now be ascertained with certainty: the thickness of the solid rocks, and of the more or less mobile strata, the existence of water-bearing or oil-bearing areas, saline and mineral deposits, seams of pure ore.

At the present time, French engineers belonging to the Compagnie générale de Géophysique, started by Conrad Schlumberger and his brother Marcel, are sending teams of geophysicists all over the world and obtaining results whose success is evidence of their importance.

These geophysicists may be regarded as forerunners; their labours are preparing the way for the explorers of the future, who will set off, like modern Jasons, to win fabulous riches in the depths of the earth.

I apologize for straying so far into the realm of underground anticipation. As we have not yet got our system of subterranean navigation and must wait for the day of its realization—man's genius may be trusted to bring it about—will you allow me, before I deal with the main subject of this chapter, to insert here a legend to fill the gap between anticipation and reality?

A very curious belief is current among the Tartars, who, from time to time, dig up skeletons of animals of enormous

size. These peasants believe that the interior of the globe
is inhabited by gigantic beasts which are able to live and
move about with ease far underground. So they are for
ever driving new ways through the bowels of the earth in
the course of their migrations and their mysterious journeyings in complete darkness, journeyings that never end,
for these strange monsters are immortal. These fabulous
creatures force their way through the ground as white ants
do, without ever coming to the surface. But if by accident
such a thing happens, the animal dies the moment it emerges
into daylight, and it is the carcasses of these beasts that man
occasionally finds in the ground.

It is a strange and moving legend this, which has
afforded a backward people with a poetic explanation of
the presence in the soil of these huge proboscidians of the
Tertiary epoch, mastodons, elephants, and mammoths.

A curious result has been that these 'giant moles'
which the Tartars in their folklore refer to under the
mysterious name of *mammantu*, suggested to the creator
of modern palaeontology, the learned Cuvier, the name of
mammoths for the great extinct pachyderms which he was
the first to study and describe.

Like the animals of the Tartar legend, man also in
certain cases finds a way of getting under the ground, and
not only in through the spacious galleries of great caves or
the gaping mouths of pot-holes, but by the same method
as the mammoths, moles, and worms.

While we are still awaiting the coming of the subterranean mode of travel I have indicated above, we have
in a sphere of activity to which scant attention has been
given, a natural bodily movement, a means of prospecting
which is so rarely employed that the only names our
language has for it are seldom used, *rampement* or *reptation*.

Reptation involves an attitude so seldom adopted by
the human race that it appears to be the fate allotted to a
few inferior creatures, a thing essentially ill suited to man,
a being of vertical habit, whose whole body and outlook is

directed skyward. Man, in fact, is only reduced to this unusual creeping posture in extreme cases, which bring him down to the level of the brute beast. When he creeps and comes nearest to the mere animal, it is from cruelty, from guile, or from cowardice; it is when he is about to make a sudden and treacherous attack on his enemy, to flee from danger, and also when the common fate of all overtakes him and he suffers and dies on the earth to whose dust he soon returns.

Yet there is another way of returning to the dust, and other and better reasons for crawling in it. You may think I am only indulging a love of paradox or pushing an enthusiasm for the underground world too far, in singing the praises of reptation. But I must defend its claims and extol its usefulness, its appeal to our imagination and our skill, and its rewards when we apply it to the study of problems and mysteries to which it has sometimes given us the key, when we have won access by crawling on our bellies in the interior of the earth to new worlds that have filled us with wonder and delight.

We find, when we go underground, that the dimensions and shapes of natural cavities in the earth vary in the most disconcerting fashion, from great spacious halls to tiny tunnels so small that there is no possibility of entering them. Of slightly larger calibre are the passages of all sorts which spelaeologists endeavour to 'force,' as they describe it, in various ways and which they refer to by characteristic names, which help us to visualize them and are full of meaning to the initiated—tunnels, bottle-necks, cat-runs, blowholes, joints, strata, squeezes, flatteners. Instead of trying to enlighten the reader as to the meaning of this terminology, in which neologisms come up against scientific terms and also names which are purely picturesque or humorous, let me try to show how the obstacles they suggest can be overcome and how it is possible to pursue such an arduous and thrilling activity as reptation underground.

Provided one knows how to crawl—for it is a thing that has to be learned—above all, if one has the will and the courage to persist at all costs, very few narrow tunnels are impossible to get through, for a man is so made that he can stretch himself out lengthways better than any animal of the same bulk in the middle. Tales of persons who have got immovably wedged in narrow passages and who, being unable to free themselves have perished there, are unhappily true enough. But these tragedies can be put down in nearly every case to the instinctive terror of being imprisoned for good, which produces a sudden stiffening and superhuman but misdirected struggles, and these are quickly followed by exhaustion; whereas it is by keeping the body supple, by slow deliberation, and above all by calm control of mind and body that I have managed to extract my person from the most repellent 'flatteners' into which I have ventured.

A child playing about, which has pushed its head between the bars of a chair or through some railings, begins all at once to struggle and yell and hurt itself simply from fear of not being able to get its head out. In its panic, some-times aggravated by that of the parent, it fails to find the particular position which enabled it to get its head through quite easily, because then it had felt its way forward; the head slipping gently through as if it were caressing the bars, without the least sign of jerkiness.

Reptation puts a considerable strain on the muscles and forces the body into positions which are extremely un-pleasant on sharp rocks, or in dust or mud, or it may be in water.

It is advisable to be as lightly clad as possible. Pockets should be previously emptied of everything in them, and on no account should the crawler wear a loose jacket, a skirt, or any piece of clothing that might catch on projec-tions, or worse still, might be rucked up if the wearer is obliged to crawl backwards. Avoidance of this danger is most important, for the turning back of a coat has been

NOTHING VENTURE!

GETTING THROUGH A CAT-RUN

known to wedge a crawler irretrievably with fatal results. There have been instances of sportsmen having crawled a few yards into a burrow and been found later dead, through having been held fixed by the wad formed by the rucking up of their clothes.

A single combination garment of coarse linen is the best for general cave work, and particularly good for reptation because of the freedom of movement it allows and because it is less apt to catch than cloth stuffs.

There are many cases, however, where one must bow to necessity and become as slim as possible, get rid of every sort of garment and crawl naked like a worm.

Creatures which live underground, such as worms and moles, have bare skins or extremely short hair on the body. In them we see a happy arrangement on the part of providence, a precaution of nature's to meet a need which man does well to imitate when he enters their particular domain. Lightly clad then or naked, head first or feet first according to circumstances, the crawler should slip into the main tunnel, placing himself on his belly, his side, or his back as the shape of the pipe-like passage demands.

Progress forward is effected either on the elbows and knees in comparatively roomy tunnels, or by propelling oneself by means of the hands folded under the chest and by movements of the feet from the ankle when the roof is extremely low. In pure reptation, movement is limited to feeble waggles of the loins, the rump, and the knees, such movements being necessarily very restricted and their range dependent on the cross section of the 'pipe.' In the final case, where the limit of human penetration is reached, individual bulk becomes an important factor, the waggles become worm-like stretchings in which alternate puffing out and drawing in of the thorax enable contracting movements to travel down the body and make it slide forwards as a cleaning sponge does in the barrel of a gun. Reptation in these cases reminds me of the way the ears of barley children put up their sleeves work along every

E

time the arm moves till they reach the shoulder, thanks to
the stiff beard of the plant.

In this final stage of crawling the arms are the worst
nuisance. When you crawl you understand why snakes
have no limbs or only limbs that are atrophied. What to
do with the arms, where to put them, how to dispose of
them—that is the biggest problem of reptation.

Held to the sides of the body the arms obviously increase
our girth; moreover, in this posture of a tied-up prisoner
one is paralysed. Stretching out the arms in front would
seem a more practical way, but, on the contrary, this only
broadens the span of the shoulders and defeats our purpose
even more than keeping the arms close to the sides. The
secret that solves the problem is to shoot one arm forward
and keep the other tight against the chest, the forearm
being folded back into the hollow of the belly. In this
position the shoulders, with one thrown forward and the
other held back, cease to form an obstacle, as they are
placed diagonally, so lessening their squareness. The
hand in front can hold the torch, feel the nature of the
ground, push away any stones or other obstructions that
might hamper or prevent further progress. The hand held
against the body helps to propel it along like a pectoral fin,
and it is this hand which has to free the clothes which may
be constantly getting caught at the level of the chest. As
for the rest of the body, it feels its way with the shoulders
and hips and has to direct itself and creep along in the
position best suited to the windings and irregularities of
the rocky tube.

It is in crawling backwards that reptation becomes a
particularly delicate operation; a right-about turn is hardly
ever possible, it is a matter of putting the engine in reverse.
It is an effort that calls for the maximum of suppleness in
movement and of patience, and imperturbable self-control
is needed when the body fails to find the one perfect position
and sticks.

It is then one appreciates and understands the need for

being undressed. Far better than nailed boots, which get
in the way and give only a vague indication of the nature
of the walls, the bare toes feel and interpret every uneven-
ness in the rock; better too than in thick clothes, which
hamper movement and are always catching on something,
the bare body, supple, smooth, and extremely compressible,
fits itself exactly to the sharp bend in the tunnel, glides
almost unconsciously into the narrowing passage, and gets
through everywhere. In such places skill and precision of
movement are indispensable.

I am prepared to admit that this man-serpent game, with
its prospect of having to lie, sometimes for hours, on nasty
cold rock, in mud or icy water, rubbing the skin off elbows,
knees, and all parts of the body, is not every one's idea of
enjoyment. Can people really be thrilled by activities so
repellent, dangerous, unhealthy, and possibly useless? Is
there not beauty and variety enough under the vault of
heaven, that a man must go and grope his way blindly at
enormous labour, plunging down deliberately into the
darkness of the nether regions and all the pitfalls it contains?

Now that is not a fair way of putting the matter. Either
a man is an underground explorer or he is not; the very
real drawbacks and undoubted dangers involved in reptation are rewarded and justified by results and sources of
satisfaction which I must put before you when I attempt to
defend these freakish performances of mine, which at first
sight must appear devoid of sense or an obvious case of
special pleading.

My very first effort at reptation was not a happy one,
though it in no way diminished my affection for caves; it
was the introductory lesson from which much had to be
learnt. The scene of this performance was the group of
small but steep-floored caves of L'Escalère, whose openings
are in the cliff at Saint-Martory, where the Garonne washes
against it.

My brother Martial and I were crawling one day in a
narrow tunnel with nothing but candles to light us. We

had taken the precaution of turning our clothes inside out, so that the traces of clay would not betray the nature of our favourite amusement to our parents. Presently a sharp turn and a very marked narrowing of the cave stopped us dead. Urged on by the demon that possesses explorers, I easily succeeded in convincing my young brother that his smaller size would enable him to get through a place that was hopeless for me to attempt. Proud of his superiority in this respect and delighted to take the lead, my seven-year-old collaborator promptly entered the fissure. Some sort of twist in it compelled him to crawl bent at the waist. Before long he began to get nervous and talked of retreating; but by dint of shouting encouragement and by more material aid, shifting his feet when they became wedged, I got him to picture the successful exit and the marvels he would assuredly find; so much so that the luckless boy managed to push his way through the tiny opening. Beyond, he could make out a hall hung with stalactities. Victory, and a magnificent discovery was ours! But these cheerful strains did not last long. Our explorer of too tender years became uneasy and anxious to return through the extremely narrow bottle-neck; he tried to hurry, got worried, and failed to find the one position which was the open sesame of this veritable keyhole. After vain attempts and an exchange of agonized appeals, I took the big step, the only effective and rational one: I went off to look for help. Cain, consumed by remorse, can hardly have been in worse case than I, as I made my way out of the cave and ran home as fast as I could. Cain had merely killed his brother, I had buried mine alive! Nevertheless, I did not dare confess my crime. I could see that a grown-up person could never get into the winding tunnel, so I seized a hammer and a steel chisel and flew back breathless to the cave, yelling to the prisoner while yet a long way off. As he had an unshakable belief in his big. brother, he had not lost his head, but waited, if not calmly, at least resignedly.

The main obstruction to his deliverance was a projecting sheet of stalactite. Luckily, it was a soft, spongy formation, which I chipped away without much difficulty with the tools I had brought. I had soon knocked away enough to let my young assistant out of his prison. He never breathed a word of our escapade and cannot have carried away too bad a memory of the day, for he subsequently became my most valuable helper.

In fact, a few years later, it was with his help that we forced the passage of an impossible-looking 'flattener' in the Montsaunès cave by pushing reptation to its furthest limits. This particular flattener was only conquered after much work with the hammer and by desperate exertions in which care had to be taken to make any small forward movement coincide with deflation of the lungs. But for this precaution the thorax would never have got through.

Some time after, when I was trying to repeat these manœuvres in a rocky tunnel known as the Trou du Téoulé, where I could only crawl along with the greatest difficulty, I was suddenly startled by finding myself face to face with a badger. Forced back into a cul-de-sac, he appeared to have made up his mind to tear my face to bits with his sharp claws. On that occasion I did my reptation full speed astern!

Small adventures like these may not appear to give much backing to my defence of reptation. But I have been dealing with first attempts; these were trials, initial ventures, but still indispensable for acquiring the experience required for the realization of bigger undertakings, for real exploration and discovery.

A tunnel may suddenly narrow, it may be filled up with earth or debris; great boulders of rock or formations of stalagmite may block it, the gaps left by joints and different strata may be very small and, worst of all, the roof may sink below water and form a siphon; such are the obstacles frequently met with underground and which interrupt the progress of many an exploring party. Every spelaeologist knows the mortification of being brought up suddenly at a turn of the tunnel by one of these obstacles, just when he thought he saw his way far ahead.

I shall not attempt here to express approval or disapproval of the clearing away of obstructions or to make any suggestions about work of this sort. I shall do no more than mention a few spells of crawling in which I have indulged, often alone and without a tool of any kind.

Efforts of this sort are apt to be extremely arduous owing to the very uncomfortable positions that have to be adopted and the confined space in which work is carried on. But for my part I do not regret the bruises, the painful stiffness, the cricks in the neck that followed bouts of crawling which were undeniably exhausting and occasionally dangerous. Small drawbacks like these do not count at all in comparison with the splendid finds I have sometimes succeeded in making and with the inward satisfaction that follows such occasions. They leave us memories which brighten our whole existence and are well worth any amount of toil and danger.

It was by diving in under the submerged roof of a subterranean stream (which I subsequently christened the Caverne de Montespan) and by forcing a way through into the continuation of this long underground watercourse, that I discovered some clay statues of lions and bears. It was a thrilling moment when we came upon these traces of human achievement moulded by the fingers of men, far older than the oldest documents of Egyptian, Syrian, or Chinese art, for their authenticity is established beyond dispute, entitling them to be called the oldest statues in the world, dating back some hundred thousand years.

In the Maladetta group of mountains on the Spanish side of the Pyrenees, which I explored alone, among other caves I entered was that of L'Escaleta, previously described by the expert Émile Belloc. In the course of a crawl there, I came to a narrow place obstructed by a lot of stones. My predecessor, who had been stopped at this point, completed his description of the place by relating a charming legend told him by his guides. According to this legend a young Aragonese shepherd succeeded in squirming through this narrow tunnel, and beyond it he discovered vast halls which had been the abode of giants. . . . Following the example of the young shepherd I set about clearing the passage. I began by demolishing the crumbling pile of stones handful after handful; but, as I dug away, other loose stuff poured down through a crack in the roof, piling up again like sand in a sandpit. The heap got bigger and bigger, and I should have given up had I not been encouraged by feeling a draught of air, very faint at first, then stronger and stronger, a sure sign there must be an extension of the cave beyond. I did, in fact, keep on till the discharge from above ceased, and slipping through the narrow window which had spat so many stones at me, I came out into a series of great halls never entered by man before. And there, to make up for the absence of the legendary giants and gold plate set out on huge stone tables, I made a great find in the shape of a whole labyrinth of shafts, an underground stream, and a way out through a narrow gap on the other side of the mountain of which nothing was known.

In the department of the Hautes-Pyrénées, the subterranean stream of Labastide, which disappears and reappears a mile and a quarter further on, was considered impossible to follow. By lying down in the water and crawling in a cramped position in the mud under a very low roof for more than forty yards, I succeeded in forcing a way out into a spacious hall and then following a passage several hundred yards long to where it ended in an underground lake. Swimming across this sheet of deep water, a distance of fifty or sixty yards, I came to a wall where a siphon enticed me on. I managed to dive through this, but a second siphon, deeper still, brought my exploration to an end.

In my book *Ten Years under the Earth* I have told how,

in the Haute-Garonne, at the foot of the Montagne de Cagire, I discovered and cleared the way into a huge cave whose existence had never been suspected, and which I christened the Grotte de Cagire.

In the famous prehistoric cave of Gargas (in the Hautes-Pyrénées), which has been known for a long time, and has been adapted for tourist traffic, I made a discovery when visiting it with the man who first roused interest in it, Bernard Suffran.   A spell of work with hammer and chisel and a trying crawl of about eighty yards enabled me to find a whole system of new caves and upper storeys hitherto unknown, which proved of the greatest interest in the study of the hydrogeological history of the place.

It was just a current of air coming out of an ordinary fox-hole, which I had to widen before I could enter it, which led to the discovery of the important and previously unknown cave of Coume-Nère in the Haute-Garonne. There I had an exciting and most unpleasant crawl through a rocky tube filled with loose earth and animals' droppings before coming out into the cave comprising tunnels, spacious chambers, a vertical range of several storeys, besides a long underground watercourse with waterfalls seventy feet high, whose exploration involved another expedition with rope ladders and a collapsible boat.   One day in the depths of this cave, I came upon an almost invisible recessed hole; and noticing a current of air was being drawn into it I decided to try and clear a passage there.

Lying flat on my stomach in this 'pipe,' and armed with a small gardening trowel, I set to work, with the help of a very keen, energetic companion, Roger Pellegrin, to scrape away the soft, sticky clay.   When the man in front had succeeded in filling a bag of earth, the man behind pulled it to him with a string and crawled away into a small chamber to empty it.   We went on working like moles in the mud for two whole nights before we had the satis-faction of creeping through and carrying our exploration a long way forward under the mountain.

In Charente, near Angoulême, a district where the few caves are generally quite unexciting, I had the luck to discover one that was full of interest and profusely decorated with the purest stalactites; it was the Grotte de Barouty (now Grotte du Quéroy). This find, like the preceding one, was made by reptation through a flattener into which no one had thought of venturing before. But there were other obstacles encountered further on in this cave which are worth mentioning. A certain cat-run set end-up like a chimney was discovered by my wife, and she incautiously forced her way into it, while I and Roger Massonnand, who joined me in this cave-exploring campaign in La Touvre, had four hours' work with hammer and chisel before we could widen the hole sufficiently to let us through. A small incident like this will give some idea of the value of slimness in spelaeology. In this same cave we met with another curious obstruction. In a narrow, slightly ascending tunnel we were stopped by a barrage of rocks through the interstices of which we could see a richly decorated chamber. Any attempt to move away the boulders would have been fatal, for with the slope in their favour they would have crushed us. By using poles to rout about in them the three of us managed to loosen the rocks, which rolled down at us one after another. But thanks to the length of our poles we had time to get out of the way whenever a collapse occurred, till the last rock was removed and the way cleared into the finest chamber in the cave.

In the cave of La Cagalière in the department of Ariège, which contains the finest crystalline formations of all this buried wonderland, I had a terrible time in a flattener and a blowhole a mile from the entrance. But once through these obstructions I came to an underground torrent which had been the object of strenuous research. I succeeded in climbing a succession of nine waterfalls and proving that this cave, some miles in length, communicates with a huge hole which I had myself discovered, explored, and christened the Gouffre Martel; it is the deepest chasm in France.

A thousand feet down this chasm a tiny tunnel has so far defeated the many desperate attempts I have made to explore it. The first time, when my wife and I reached the depth of a thousand feet, we were stopped where the passage narrowed to a small hole into which a stream of water disappeared. Despite all I could do, with all my clothes off, I could not get into this narrow water-pipe. As it was winter there was more than three feet of snow at the entrance of the chasm, which is at a height of over six thousand five hundred feet, and the temperature of the water was one degree centigrade. Later on I returned to the bottom of the chasm with my friend and colleague the Belgian physicist Max Cosyns. This time I had brought a watertight rubber suiting and was able to work for a long spell lying in the icy water. After an hour's hard work, in the course of which I dug out with my hands a sort of channel through the stony sediment and was able to crawl forward some forty yards, my efforts had exhausted me, and I returned crawling backwards with a great effort. Half-way back I butted into my friend, who was on his way to meet me and relieve me at the task of clearing the road. In spite of all our efforts we could not succeed in passing each other, so we emerged from the flooded tunnel like a couple of water-rats from their holes.

I returned to the attack for the third time with Gaston Giscard of the Société Spéléologique de France. It was raining on this occasion and consequently there was a possibility of a sudden rise in the stream, through whose course underground I was about to crawl with only a narrow space between the water and the roof. So, before creeping in on my stomach, I had tied to my ankle a string which my friend, keeping watch at the mouth of the pipe, was to unroll as I advanced. Three jerks of the string were to give me warning of any flooding and tell me to return at once. Signalling by shouts or whistles is useless in a low winding pipe like this one. Having reached the terminus of my previous advance I set to work once more, laboriously digging out my channel with the help of a steel gadget specially forged for the purpose, a sort of mole's claw attached to the wrist by a leather strap, for the tunnel was too narrow to let me use a tool with a handle, however short.

I worked away for a good long time and had gained some yards, when I noticed that the signalling string which we had agreed should be kept constantly taut was slack. Drawing it to me I gathered in ten yards or so and then found it had been frayed and cut in two by an edge of rock. The end Giscard was holding had twisted itself round a spike of rock and so gave him the false impression he had still got me on a lead.

The rain had, in fact, been making the stream rise, but the distress signals were intercepted by this wretched rock, while the end of the string tied to my foot was trailing freely and was dangerously inoperative.

Max, pulling conscientiously at the string, felt the resistance of the rock which he imagined to be my leg, and could not account for my rash obstinacy and failure to obey the signal we had agreed upon. It might be described as a pretty sharp warning, when one has come within an ace of being drowned in an icy stream a thousand feet under the earth.

In Morocco, in the Gouffre de Frégate in the Djebel-Chiker massif, my wife and I were stopped eighty feet down by a pile of rocks through which came a gentle current of air. Our efforts to effect a clearance were eventually crowned with success, so that we were able to reach a depth of six hundred feet, the greatest depth yet reached in any chasm in the Middle Atlas or in Africa.

To prolong the list of reptations and clearings of tunnels might only weary the reader, for such episodes gain nothing in the telling, though there is a thrill and a charm about adventures like these quite beyond the knowledge of those who have never lived through them.

What spelaeologist worthy of the name has not at one time or another broken the seals of one of these closed domains, forcing his way in by painful contortions and at great risk through the narrowest of gates? To recall every exploit and every discovery is obviously impossible. But it is hard to refrain from addressing a word of brotherly remembrance to the colleagues who shared the toil and knew the thrill of delight that rewarded a new find. To the three Begouen brothers, who forced their way through the cat-run that had resisted attack in the Pyrenean cave of Le Tuc d'Audubert and had the joy of discovering traces of prehistoric man, including the famous group of the two clay bisons, a masterpiece of prehistoric sculpture. To Robert de Joly, who has won his way so often through flatteners and effected clearances in the exploration of hundreds of caves and pot-holes, some of them of the first importance. And to every spelaeologist who on some occasion or other has torn down a veil and revealed an unknown cavern.

Everywhere, and with increasing frequency, fresh discoveries are rewarding those who have faced the unpleasant and often thankless task of worming their way into apertures which have been passed by or considered impracticable. And everywhere the crawlers underground become devotees of this sport, which offers them an adventurous and original way to discover something new, to experience new and exciting sensations, and to collect memories that do not fade.

Having come to the end of this apology of reptation, let me say how fully conscious I am that words are quite inadequate to produce the atmosphere of the many exciting situations and thrilling sights which are beyond description. But what a poignant thrill of satisfaction there is in overcoming fears and difficulties, in discovering new fields for exploration, in finding from time to time the confirmation of a hypothesis laboriously thought out, in watching

Nature's mysterious forces at work, and finally in seeing that even the darkest depths underground bear traces of the finger of God.

That is what I want the reader to feel and to love about this science of spelaeology, which has a mystery and a poetry of its own.

As he struggles among the prehistoric, barbed entanglements of stalactites, panting and groaning in the sticky mud, apparently still wet from the waters of the flood, the crawler, more than any other man, can feel that special quality of joy in discovery, that dreamlike impression of being the first man to make his appearance in a place where no human foot had trod since the beginning of the world.

In this rude struggle which mind and body carry on with material things, the explorer underground 'va dans l'immensité noire portant devant lui son cœur comme un flambeau,' [1] keeping always in the forefront of his thoughts that fine crawler's motto: *Ad augusta per angusta* (To mighty ends by narrow ways).

[1] Pierre Termier, *La Vocation de savant.*

4

NOTHING WORSE THAN A FRIGHT

Le courage, c'est parfois d'avoir peur et d'être le seul à le savoir.

The adventure I am going to describe happened to me after I had returned unscathed to the delights of peace, when I had resumed my studies at Toulouse, which had been broken off by the war of 1914–18. I also proceeded to carry on with great energy the researches and explorations underground which had been similarly interrupted.

Every Saturday evening I used to take the train for the Pyrenees, where I was born, bound for some region rich in caves, where I hoped to arrive at nightfall. I would then hurry on with a rucksack in the direction of some cave I particularly wanted to explore and prepare to sleep there. For years I had been used to spending the night in the open in pretty uncomfortable conditions and was well hardened to the inclemencies of the weather. This sort of return to nature in my habits put me in the right kind of atmosphere for my researches about cave-men, and at the same time gave me more time to devote to them. The cold of the night and the discomfort of the bivouac often kept me awake, and I did some of my exploring at night, so that occasionally, by sunrise, I had not slept much, but had carried out a thorough exploration of a cave and had made some interesting observations and reflections in the doubly deep night of the earth and of the cave. I had then the whole day before me to look for other caverns underground and find out all about them, staying there to explore their hidden recesses.

One evening in May, on arriving for one of these expeditions at Tarascon-sur-Ariège, I realized as I came out of the station that in the hurry of leaving at Toulouse, I had forgotten to put in the few provisions that generally kept company in the rucksack with the bread, the acetylene lamp, and the candles. In one of the streets of old Tarascon, dating from the Middle Ages, I went into a grocer's wine-shop to get what I wanted, and there a man in a blue apron was serving out many-coloured alcoholic drinks to a group of ruffianly-looking Spaniards. My selection was soon made, but when it came to paying for my modest purchases I found I had no small change of any kind in my pocket, so I had to pull out from the innermost depths of my pocket-book some bank notes, which I rather foolishly kept there at the risk of losing notes and pocket-book together in some cave or other. I mention these details because they had a considerable bearing on the ensuing events I am about to describe. The grocer, having no change himself, sent his wife out to get some and the delay gave the fellow, who was a bit of a gossip and full of curiosity, a chance to ask me a lot of questions. I am used to exciting curiosity in the natives by my equipment and the nature of my researches, and rage in the local dogs by the stick I carry, and have made it a rule always to explain quite openly the nature and objects of my quest. As this particular fellow was something of a sportsman himself and wanted precise details, I ended by revealing all my programme, which comprised sleeping that night in the Grotte de Pradières, more than three thousand feet up in the Montagne du Soudour, in order to be at work early the next morning.

I spare you the exclamations of this peaceful sportsman of Tarascon so reminiscent of that immortal Nimrod of the real Tarascon by the Rhône. Having at last pocketed my change, I left the shop. The Spaniards had remained silent, never betraying the smallest sign of interest, while I emerged into the street followed by an endless torrent of earnest exhortation poured out for my benefit by the grocer, whose comfortable complacency I had disturbed, so that I had to hurry off, cursing my frankness.

As I left the small town, I was pleased to see it was a lovely still night. The moon was high in the sky and promised its light for the first part of my journey and the climb I had to make. After walking about three miles, I left the deserted road and began a stiff ascent over a long shale slope where loose stones covered the whole side of the mountain. By midnight my climb had ended at the entrance to the cave. It is a vast portico which opens dramatically in the face of a cliff, whence there is a fine view over the valley and the country round, and just inside, hidden from observation, is a spacious chamber with a lofty roof. Its floor is raised up in places into strange lumps of hard clay that look like old ant-hills.

I searched for a good spot to lie down on and settled myself on the floor at the extreme edge at the brink of the cave, close to the slope outside which falls to the valley bottom. I lay on my back with my coat collar turned up, using my rucksack as a pillow, enjoying the perfect sense of relaxation that follows a stiff climb, while my eyes wandered from the dark vault of the cave to the starry vault of heaven.

In the stillness of the night my ears were sensitive to the slightest sounds: the drops of water dripping slowly from the rocky ceiling, the occasional faint twitterings of birds nesting in crevices and pockets in the walls. In such a setting it was only natural to compare my present situation with that of prehistoric man, the cave-man, who must once, thousands of years ago, have spent the night like me, watching and dreaming at the entrance to the same cave in the same surroundings. Did he perhaps think about the future, whereas I was trying to picture the earliest ages of man's existence?

The moon had by this time disappeared and the night was very dark. Great gleams of light and heavy growls of thunder in the direction of the Pic des Trois Seigneurs —the monarch of the district—broke in on my thoughts, or rather, gave them a new direction. The lightning

RAOUL CASTERET CRAWLING IN THE GARGAS CAVE

A BARRIER OF STALACTITES

flashing furtively on the snows of this high peak, the distant rumbling of the storm echoing among the hills, brought me back from twenty thousand years ago to the years just past, when the flashes and the thunder of the guns had filled my ears. Stretched on the ground as I used to be in the long war when men lived and when so many died in close contact with mother earth, lying at full length beside my alpenstock and rucksack as I used to lie beside rifle and haversack, my thoughts went back to those battlefields that had hardly yet grown cold. Alone as I was, watching like a sentry in the night as the storm rapidly drew near, all the most vivid memories of the war came back to me.

Then came the rain, adding its frenzy to the thunder, and I witnessed the sight, always an impressive one, of a storm at night in the mountains, with the thunder crashing and reverberating through the great marble hall behind me till I fancied all the devils in hell had met together there. The clouds were low, and being high up myself, I was in the middle of the storm. The lightning flashed ceaselessly, and the crackling discharges seemed to run over me and make the ground tremble. These mystical, wild manifestations of nature speak a language that can make the toughest men shudder and stir the least imaginative minds. Some men, moreover, prefer these violent outbursts of nature, when her face is convulsed by the fury of a storm, to smiling country and melodious sounds of peaceful life.

The gusts of rain were driving in on me, so I had to withdraw a short way inside the cave. At last the storm passed away towards the Tabe massif, lightening the horizon there with its flashes; the rain stopped, peace returned and with it the stars. I looked up and measured the advance of the different constellations since my arrival on the spot. Of what small account was this sudden storm beside the immutably controlled motion of those distant worlds; how feeble my powers of thought beside the eternal problem of the Infinite!

F

And then, just when my mind, shaken by the storm, was becoming lulled into a peaceful sleep, a slight noise, faint though it was, caught my attention. When one is alone with nature, the senses are unconsciously on the alert and recover some of the vigilance and quickness of perception that must have belonged to our primitive ancestors.

Far below me there had been a movement of the stones on the huge shale slopes that cover this side of the mountain. It might be due to the descending streamlets resulting from the heavy storm; besides, in these nightly vigils among the mountains, mysterious noises are heard which are not usually noticed; they are merely evidence of a slow process of disintegration which is infinitesimal in degree, but continuous; stones break off and fall and roll down the slope; particles of snow slide down; glaciers split; the murmurs of waterfalls and streams are hushed by the night frost, gusts of wind get up and suddenly die down.

With ears cocked and eyes wide open, I tried to think what this puzzling noise might be. The slight tinkle made by hitting small slabs of limestone was followed by the rustle of shifting shale; it sounded as if some animal were traversing the great slopes of stones I had climbed some hours before. A fox would have made less noise; the wolf no longer inhabits the Pyrenees; the bear is met with, it is true, in the big mountain forests, but not among the rocks of Le Soudour, where you have difficulty in finding a tree of any kind. As for the chamois, there could be no question of that at such a comparatively low altitude. Among the fauna of the Pyrenees, the wild boar was the only possible solution. The hammering of hard hoofs was, in fact, becoming clearer and more recognizable, which would not be so in the case of a soft-footed animal like a dog. The presence of such an animal—the boar being one of the last wild beasts left in Europe—carried my thoughts back again to past ages when most formidable animals inhabited the forests and steppes which were later to become our own country of France.

The furtive advance of this beast in the night awoke in me a vague sort of regret for those wild times when primitive man had to struggle for thousands of years against ferocious beasts always on the watch for him and attacking him even in the caves he lived in. What courage and what strange devices our Stone Age ancestors—those most valiant huntsmen of all time—must have needed to attack and get the better of the mammoth, the lion, the giant bear, the bison, and the packs of wolves! What murderous fights—locked, as they must have been, in savage embrace—were fought, before they triumphed over such formidable foes as these, with nothing but the rudest stone weapons!

As I was picturing these hunting scenes and the terrors of that distant age of fear, and thanking the pachyderm below for having by his presence carried me back in fancy to prehistoric times, I was surprised to notice that the animal seemed to be getting nearer and was climbing up towards the cave. My surprise, I must confess, gave way to some anxiety when it became evident that the brute was coming closer and closer. I could now make out quite clearly the noise of the hoofs striking and leaving the moving stones, the motion being interrupted by short pauses.

I realized that in another moment the boar would burst into the cave and would scent my presence. As it was a solitary beast, it would presumably be an aggressive one that would run at me. Now, as usual, I carried no weapon, nor was there any tree or place of refuge within reach. I managed to keep my head all right, and was even able to spare a thought for my prehistoric huntsman, who could hardly have been worried at all by the visit of a mere boar; but I admit I have no experience of encounters of this sort, or of how to deal with them, when they occur!

The beast was barely twenty yards away and had just reached a thicket in front of the entrance of the cave. I could already hear the branches in front rustling when the impressive silence of the night was shattered by a violent though partially checked sneeze, which petrified me. Matters had suddenly become serious, for it was a man who had sneezed, and what on earth was he here for at such an hour?

Why this silent approach without a lantern, betrayed by this sudden involuntary sneeze? Suggestions came crowding into my mind, and one clear logical explanation emerged; I was to be surprised and attacked. By whom? By one of the Spaniards who had seen my bank notes when he was drinking in the pub last night.

His late arrival would be due to the storm, which must have stopped him on the way. At that moment, while the knave was lying low after the untimely sneeze that had given him away, I distinctly heard several other persons climbing up the shale slope. It was a well-organized ambush in a place where there was no chance whatever of any help. What was I to do?

I took advantage of the few moments remaining before the concerted attack began to grope my way further into the cave. I crossed the vast entrance hall in complete darkness, staggering about among the numerous rocks, and pushed on into the depths of the cave, at the risk of dropping into a crevasse or one of the pits which are of frequent occurrence underground. I wandered on at random in the pitchy darkness, for I had to avoid showing any sort of light, till I stopped at a place where the roof got so low I should have had to crawl. I lay down at full length under the low roof unable to get any further in and decided to remain there lying low. During my hurried retreat with its numerous collisions I had had no time to think of how my pursuers were getting on. No doubt they were now looking for me.

I wonder how long I remained cowering in my hiding-place, in constant expectation that my enemies would burst in and my presence be revealed by the beam of a lantern. The moments of dreadful suspense were long, and then, extraordinary as it appears, I fell asleep, though it was a troubled sleep.

When I woke up, stiff all over, the curious attitude I was in was sufficient evidence that I had not been dreaming. I waited a moment to consider the position and decide what I had better do.   By the light of a match I made out it was four o'clock and that I was crouching in a low-roofed cul-de-sac.   The impressive silence so characteristic of the cave world was untroubled save for the faint musical notes made by drops of water falling from the roof.   I love this melodious sound and it somewhat restored my serenity of mind; I realized that my manœuvre had been a wise one, and that my attackers had had to give up the search. I fell into an optimistic mood, filled with a new enthusiasm for these Pyrenean caves, in whose depths I had lived so many unforgettable hours, and one of which had just provided me with a haven of refuge.

After much anxious consideration I decided to venture outside where daylight would soon be appearing.   For the first time that night I lit a candle and, screening the flame behind my fingers as a precaution, I set about finding my way out of the cave.

This cave of Pradières is rather over two hundred yards in length, but I had not gone to the end, but only into a recess, so it was not long before I recognized the great entrance hall.   From the cavernous depths I was still in, I could just see, under the mighty arch of the hall, the diffused light of dawn.   I blew out the candle and picked a way over a chaotic collection of rocks.   A moment later I found myself in the middle of the hall, still only partly reassured, and on the look-out for the slightest noise, or the least sign of a suspicious dark patch.   And then, just as I came round one of the pseudo ant-hills on the floor, which I had noticed the previous evening, several forms came simultaneously into view, stood up with terrifying suddenness and galloped off, charging madly into each other as they went, and waking all the echoes of the huge vault above me.

It was the most violent and, happily, the last of the

various emotions of this troubled night; I had not succeeded in identifying the shadowy forms which I had
barely seen before they vanished at my approach.

I advanced to the edge at the entrance where the slope
fell away to the valley, and there, twenty yards below me,
I saw five wretched sheep with heads upraised, five
silhouetted forms, caught in the attitude of curiosity and
panic, still trembling from the sudden fright I had inflicted
on them. They must have taken me for a bear! Any-
how, it was their turn to be frightened, after keeping me
in a panic all night, having taken them for men. The
storm in the night had caught them out in the open where
these animals spend several months of the year roaming
about at will. Soaked and shivering after the exceptionally
heavy storm, they had come from a distance to shelter under
the great arch they knew so well. It was their arrival and
their ascent of the shale slope that had caused all the
excitement. As for the sneeze which had given me such
a fright, I was mortified to learn that same evening that
sheep cough and sneeze just like the human animal. I
could not bear them any malice, so I put all the seduction
I could into my voice and gestures as I cried: 'Saou, saou,'
stretching out my arms to them as shepherds in the
Pyrenees do when they offer salt to their flocks.

Recognizing the form of a man and hearing the magic
syllables, my five sheep were instantly reassured and came
up to me. Standing under the vast portico as the sun
rose, with my hands open as though I had a gift to bestow,
and at my feet the eager creatures with outstretched necks
and great beseeching eyes, I felt like an enchanter, and
thought of the legend of Saint Julian the Hospitaller, who
could cast a spell on any animal. I freely forgave the
timid beasts my vanished terrors of the night. For once
in my life I felt inclined to embrace a sheep!

PART TWO

THE REALMS BELOW

La vie des savants nous enseigne, à chaque page, que les grandes vérités n'ont été découvertes et établies que par des études prolongées, solitaires, dirigées constamment vers un objet spécial, guidées sans cesse par une logique méfiante et réservée.

CUVIER.

Every page in the life-history of the great masters teaches us that the greatest truths have been discovered and confirmed only by prolonged, solitary research, persistently directed to a definite end, always kept in the right path by refusal to accept any guidance but that of close, watchful reasoning.

I

SPELAEOLOGY

Speak to the earth and it shall teach thee.

Job xii. 8.

A chapter with a very repellent name! And at the
outset, before I proceed to tell you about the underground
world of which I have made a life-study, let me confess
that I am but an amateur, a title it needs courage to wear
in France, where, despite the independence we show in our
ideas and in our characters, we do not suffer gladly those
who are self-taught, the *francs-tireurs* of science.

For this reason I am not going to talk as a technician,
but as a dilettante, for I do not want to lead the reader
along the path of stern research, but rather take him, if
possible, on a pleasure outing in the cave country.

Spelaeology, or the science of caves, is a late arrival
among the many branches of human knowledge, a far more
varied and exciting branch than is generally believed, for
deep down in the earth are things to astonish and to thrill
the most blasé of men, to stimulate the dreams of the poet
and the philosopher, as well as plenty of material to excite
and perplex the expert.

The thousands of caves and pot-holes now known
represent but a tiny fraction of the far larger and more
numerous cavities which have no outlet to the world above,
but which are there in the secret places of the earth; a
tremendous mineral domain of which we can explore only
the antechamber. Spelaeology includes the study not only
of the formation and evolution of cave systems, but of
everything which can be observed and studied underground.

As is the case with many other scientific achievements,
the preliminary observations and the earliest investigations

81

were carried out by obscure forerunners, who were drawn below the surface by considerations other than scientific.

It was so with our distant ancestors, the cave-men, who first went underground to try to find some haven of refuge from the cold and inclemencies of weather and from ferocious beasts.

These were the first spelaeologists, pursuing after their fashion a utilitarian spelaeology, to which we probably owe our existence to-day, for without it the human species could doubtless never have survived the rigours of the Ice Age.

When he first appeared on the globe, man seems to have led a comparatively easy, lazy sort of life. In a warm damp climate, rather like the present tropical variety, he lived mainly on the fruits he picked, without bothering about clothes and satisfied with putting up rude huts made of branches from the trees. Later on, an extension of the ice sheets, resulting, it is thought, from a change of inclination of the earth's axis, produced a sad upset on the globe.

The period known as the Ice Age caused a climatic cataclysm which made an end of many animal species and came as a shock to the human being who had hitherto lived a free and easy life, compelling him to seek refuge in caves. Only there could our ancestors protect themselves against the awful cold which was to hold sway for thousands of years and compel them to become troglodytes.

Faced with the invading ice and its deadly cold, primitive man stole like a rat into any crack or hollow in the ground and so discovered and annexed the underground world. This was also the time when man lived, in every sense of the word, the darkest hours of his history. It was a savage epoch, this age of cold and terror, in which man, all but naked and with only the rudest of weapons, had to struggle against a murderous climate as well as against fierce animals of enormous size, which fought him for the possession of his subterranean shelters.

Down there in the caves, which they explored to depths

which still astonish us when we think of the primitive
lighting which was all they had, these prehistoric men
carried on a precarious existence, yet not as mere wild
brutes, as was long supposed and as some think, even to-day.

The cave-man, with all his lamentably low standard of
material comfort, and despite his heavy burden of distress
and suffering, was still *homo sapiens*. It was he, with
hostile nature all around him, who rescued humanity from
the savagery of preceding ages.

The traces of him found in caves enable us to reconstruct
and understand the manners, the psychology, and aspira-
tions of this remote ancestor of ours; burials carefully and
touchingly performed, even in the case of infants, memorial
engravings of hands mutilated to show grief, ingeniously
made objects, frescoes, and sculptures of animals showing
an amazing technique and realism, and whose inspiration
has its origin in magic, showing evidence of spiritual
anxieties and spiritual needs. It all shows that these men
who hunted the mammoth, the bison, and the reindeer
were able to carry out their immense and sacred task, that
of winning and safeguarding in the darkest of all ages the
title of lords of creation and—if the expression is permissible—of being themselves their ancestors.

We shall never know what this heroic era was like;
man survived those thousands of years by his clever devices,
his endurance, and perhaps from his faith in better times
to come. As pariahs they fought their way through life
with all their energy and their unsharpened wits, in the
midst of geological upheavals on a planet already old but
still in travail.

How often, in those past ages when melancholy and
despair must have added to the difficulties and dangers of
every kind, must our early ancestor have crouched in the
entrance of his cave, mounting guard over it, with his
thoughts wandering among the stars. What worries came
to agitate his mind, what hopes and thoughts passed
through it?

He had reason to fear the sudden appearance of some formidable great beast, he had to defend his tribe, his family, to see the fire, his only source of heat and life, did not go out; he had to anticipate and avert the starvation that might follow on his exodus to some far country or on the disappearance of game driven away or exterminated by the cold.   There are evidences miraculously preserved in the depths of certain caves which afford abundant proof that this same man believed in a whole mysterious pantheon, the secret of whose nature has for ever perished with him, that he was in communication with occult divinities and powers whom he conceived and invoked in times of dire distress.

Those lonely meditations in the silent depths of caves and in the long vigils of the night were certainly potent elements in the growth of his intellectual and spiritual life. That solitude, which the poet tells us 'concentrates and strengthens the faculties of the mind,' must have been an important factor in raising man's moral standard and stirring a desire for better things.

Much later, as a result of a new change in the position of the earth, the climate became milder and the rise of temperature disposed of the mantle of ice covering the ground.   Then at last the troglodyte was able to leave his underground retreat and live a free life in the warm spring sun of that golden age.   The civilization which had been so long preparing in secret, potentially present in the mind of man, was to burst forth in its fullness.   Coming out of the holes under the earth, as the larva emerges from the chrysalis in the form of the perfect insect, man had a chance of showing what he could do.

With feverish industry and great ingenuity he built strange lacustrine cities.   With fervent enthusiasm he set about his first attempts at culture; he tried to tame and rear some of the animals, and with his most wonderful discovery of all, the use of metals, he at last had weapons and tools worthy of himself, with which to begin the conquest of the world.

From that moment the now deserted caves gradually came to be regarded in the minds of men as places accursed, full of dangers and of animals and spirits that were malevolent. They rarely returned to these places where they had suffered such cruel hardships. Henceforth no one ventured into them. Tradition only kept alive the remembrance of cave life and the mysterious ceremonies that went on there in the dark ages when the human race was accursed.

The persistent and widespread nature of this tradition is evident from the undeniable fact that throughout the ages the cave has been regarded as a sacred and also as an accursed place, the abode of all forms of imaginary powers, the gods of the nether regions, the spirits of ancestors, the souls of the departed, genies, fairies, and dragons.

After certain caves had been consecrated, a further, curious development made its appearance; sorcerers and fetish men dug out, carved, and decorated artificial openings in the earth or set up monuments manifestly inspired by cave mentality: burial grottoes, dolmens, covered ways, tumuli, underground vaults, and sepulchres. The most important and strangest monuments of this kind, besides the countless dolmens distributed all over the world, are the *speos* of Egypt, the temple of Ipsambul; in India the marvellous underground chambers of Ellora, Salsette, and Elephanta, and the many underground temples in widely different countries, including our catacombs, crypts, and burial vaults.

All this architecture, built in the likeness of primitive man's cave dwellings, has its source in the vague but tenacious memory of these early stages of human history. The connection between prehistoric and modern times, suggested by the survival of this memory, is often fragile, diminished almost to vanishing point, but yet still discernible by those who have learned to pick up the traces that remain.

It was a trapper named Hutchins, who, pursuing a

wounded bear, discovered in 1809 the Mammoth Cave in the U.S.A., the largest known cave in the world. In 1842 another hunter, Bonnemaison, when clearing the entrance to a burrow, found the famous cave of Aurignac in the Haute-Garonne, which revealed a remarkable period in the civilization of the Stone Age and gave its name to the Aurignacian Epoch, one of the most important in prehistoric times. It was a shepherd, Sahuquet, who, in tracking down a fox, ventured into a narrow, winding tunnel and came out into a great cave. He ran out terrified, shouting that he had just entered the vestibule of hell. What he had actually discovered was the immense cave of Dargilan in Lozère.

To another shepherd we owe the discovery of the caves of the Eisriesenwelt, the greatest ice caverns known. This humble forerunner was attracted to the caves by the feathery cloud of mist which at certain times rises from this system of caves, a great maze of eighteen miles of underground passages extending under the Austrian Alps. In 1901 the cowboy Jim White discovered the huge caves of Carlsbad in the U.S.A. in a very remarkable way. Riding along at sundown, he saw in the far distance a cloud of smoke coming up out of the ground. Thinking it was due to a volcanic eruption he turned tail and galloped away as hard as he could. Next day, curiosity took him back to the spot, and going closer, he found the entrance to a cave and the cause of the phenomenon he had witnessed the day before; it was a cloud of bats which flew out every evening in the twilight and which he had mistaken for a column of smoke. In the southern states and in Mexico these creatures are indeed found in prodigious numbers.

Mythologies, which may pass for summaries of immemorial traditions, abound in wonderful stories about caves. The writers of the ancient world, Pliny, Seneca, Plutarch, Homer, Virgil, Herodotus, Plato, Aristotle, seem often to be inspired by dim ancestral memories in the way they deal with the world beneath their feet. But that world had to wait long for the day of rediscovery, when the science of spelaeology, resuscitated from prehistoric times, was brought to birth again by a few bold fore-runners, who dared to break the spell and brave the curse which had fallen on the castles of the Sleeping Beauty, by which I mean the caves, the deep chasms, the underground rivers. It was, therefore, only recently that human interest in caves awoke once more; and a few humble pioneers prepared the way for the experts who were to describe and prove the value of this new branch of natural science.

By some happy dispensation of providence, so often found presiding over human progress, the men who first happened to direct the course and share the victories of spelaeological sciences were just humble experimentalists. In fact, the first to make any systematic examination of unexplored caves appear to have been treasure-hunters drawn there by the lure of the fabulous riches which persistent legends have pictured lying in caves in all parts of the world. Hunters, too, occupy an important place in these early discoveries and explorations. And here we link up with the men of prehistoric times, who made adventurous expeditions underground in pursuit of game and in their search for less accessible quarters.

Other forerunners, whose discoveries were less sensa-tional, but who braved the terrors of the underworld, deserve mention. Among them were the cragsmen who went after ravens and other birds of prey nesting in holes in cliffs or in pot-holes; bone collectors, who were let down into deep pits to harvest from them carcasses to make animal charcoal; men looking for saltpetre, long used in the manufacture of gunpowder; crystal-hunters who carried on their perilous trade in precipitous mountains and caves containing stalactites.

Even before them, other forerunners had occasionally made use of caves. Wizards in country districts would perform their incantations underground, where their weird scribblings have been found traced on the rocks. Brigands and secret societies took refuge there, as well as coiners, whose primitive workshops have been found in the depths of caverns. Refugees too, deserters and outlaws, victims of persecution, often found a safe asylum underground, whilst hermits and lovers of solitude of their own free choice occasionally selected a cave for their abode.

In the tracks of these forerunners and sometimes on information given by them, there presently appeared experts who, each following his own line of action, devoted themselves to a methodical study of openings in the earth's surface, showing the working of subterranean streams, describing and explaining all kinds of phenomena which had hitherto been unknown or inexplicable. The earliest of these experts seem to have been naturalists, who made a study of the bones of animals called antediluvian, discovered by quarrymen. These naturalists opened the way for the palaeontologists, who dug up from the floors of caves the skeletons of the huge beasts of the Quaternary Period.

One of the first, who has good claims to be considered the creator of the science of palaeontology, afterwards developed by Cuvier, was Esper, who as early as 1777 was exploring the caves in Franconian Switzerland.

Under the same conditions and in the same manner as the naturalists, anthropologists and students of prehistoric man carried out patient researches in the numerous deposits and signs of habitation he had left in caves. By a careful study of the various layers of these deposits they slowly and surely arrived at results which were checked, and which enabled them to draw up a detailed chronology of the different stages of the Stone Age. The oldest human skeletons were discovered and studied, the carvings and paintings on rock walls were revealed, and so was built up a picture, such as had not previously been dreamed of, of the sort of life lived by our remote ancestors. And as the historians of primitive man had done, geologists and mineralogists proceeded underground, to study the manner

LETTING HIM DOWN

AT THE ENTRANCE TO THE COUME-NERE CAVE

of formation of caves and of the sparkling ornaments of crystal they contain.

With these last, we enter the period of exploration in the strict sense of the word. Physicists and chemists turned their attention to the many phenomena that occur in caves, whilst botanists, biologists, and entomologists revealed the existence of a strange and interesting flora and fauna peculiar to caves.

Hydraulic engineering, agriculture, and the hydro-electric industry had to pay attention, and very particular attention, to subterranean systems of water circulation, whether in order to utilize or create underground reservoirs or to drain unhealthy districts into systems of caverns (as has been done on a great scale in the Peloponnese), or even to bring to the surface and make practical use of under-ground streams for the purpose of irrigation or the provision of electric energy.

It was found, too, that certain caves contain important amounts of phosphates resulting from the accumulation of animals' bones, a natural source of wealth which is being vigorously developed.

Some shrewd individuals also found a source of profit in facilitating access to specially picturesque caves and so encouraging sightseers. This by-product of spelaeology, the profit from tourists, has become a considerable source of revenue in many districts. And finally, the expert in hygiene, in the person of the famous explorer and geologist Martel, by showing how the underground water systems work, has revealed the terrible danger of pollution and poisoning to which such waters are liable, when dead animals and filth are thrown into pot-holes and the count-less cracks and hollows that gape open at the surface. It is a most reprehensible and dangerous and also a universal practice, and this great Frenchman has been tireless in waging war against it. His efforts have at last made people understand how absolutely essential it is to avoid contaminating underground springs, and to set up barriers

G

round the gathering grounds of water intended for human consumption.

With the advance and accumulation of knowledge an improved technique came into use for the exploration of the underground world. In the early days the pioneers used to push their explorations forward by the light of old-fashioned torches or candles. Later explorers were provided with oil lamps and finally with acetylene and electric lamps. For descents into vertical holes they abandoned the simple rope worked by hand from a windlass, with the explorer dangling at the end seated on a sort of trapeze.

A combination of rope ladders and a spare rope has become the classic method of descent. Martel was the first to make use of a portable telephone in place of signals conveyed by shouts or whistles, which frequently proved quite inadequate. The exploration of a cave, however big, requires quite a modest outfit, unless it comprises shafts and passages at different levels or an underground river. But when a descent is undertaken into a chasm many hundred feet deep, the difficulties become serious, and such descents involve the employment of an outfit which is both costly and tiresome to transport.

The exploration of the deepest holes known, reaching depths of nearly two thousand feet, has only been made possible by numerous expeditions prepared in the greatest detail by specialists who rivalled one another in courage and persistence. Some idea of the extensive outfit used may be gathered from the fact that during the exploration of one of the deepest of these holes, the fearsome Bertarelli chasm in Istria, a violent storm caused a flood underground which drowned two of the spelaeologists and resulted in loss of apparatus of various kinds valued at two thousand pounds.

In France, where we have been the first, with the Austrians, to make a serious science of spelaeology, a Spelaeological Society was formed in 1895, which published an account of underground exploration in the country, systematically carried out by Martel, his colleagues, and his disciples.

This master of spelaeology did not confine his efforts to France; he visited various distant countries to pursue his studies, to bring to light unknown caves and clear up spelaeological problems, sacrificing health, energy, and money in the course of his innumerable researches. What he had mainly in view was the new and important geological aspect of caves, the manner of their formation, and the part they have played; and the question of how hydrogeology can be applied in matters of public health and in industry. In masterly fashion he codified and developed in many great works this far-reaching, fruitful, and enthralling science of spelaeology. It was Martel who gave to this science a far greater and more beneficent field of study, revealing and explaining in the clearest and most practical way which compelled acceptance the very complicated mechanism and the very extensive work of underground springs.

The war of 1914 put a sudden end to the work of the rapidly developing Spelaeological Society and it did not survive. It was not till 1930 that it was resuscitated by a group of young people led by M. de Joly. He is an engineer as well as an explorer, who has visited hundreds of caves and deep pot-holes, and he is himself the inventor and maker of improved apparatus and gadgets which have enabled him, thanks also to his courageous enterprise, to carry out successfully certain bits of exploration which had up till then been regarded as impracticable. Thanks to this new equipment, with which his colleagues are now provided, spelaeological exploration in France is entering on a new era.

At the present day (1939) spelaeology is enjoying a great vogue. A large group of young people, whose greed for some new and violent sensation is stimulated by what is risky and unknown, is keenly investigating what is underground. There are organized meets in pot-holes and caves; in all parts of the country there are sections affiliated to the Société Spéléologique de France, and an eager search is carried on for new caves and new, yawning chasms.

It would take too long and would certainly be premature to attempt to give a record of the principal results that have been achieved. I shall, therefore, keep within the plan and title of my book which makes no claim to treat of spelaeology in general, and shall confine myself to the Pyrenees, the scene of most of my own activities.

The chain, from its humblest foothills to its highest summits, is exceptionally rich in the number and interest of its underground chasms. Its caves have been used for human habitation and so, like the prehistoric centre of Les Eyzies in Dordogne, are the happiest of hunting grounds for students of that captivating creature, prehistoric man. Many of the Pyrenean caves have revealed important prehistoric centres of human life, and famous deposits which have furnished treasures to our principal museums. Fifteen of these caves are decorated with drawings, frescoes, and even pieces of sculpture, which comprise the oldest known documentary examples of writing and art, many, many times older than the oldest known civilizations of Egypt or China.

Without attempting to enumerate all these caves or the men who discovered them (they are far too numerous and I have not sufficient written evidence to do it properly) I must just mention Aurignac, Gargas, Bédeilhac, Niaux, Lombrives, Lherm, Sabart, Enlène, Le Mas-d'Azil. Among these Gargas, Bédeilhac, Niaux came into the news a second time, when there were discovered in their depths examples of the type of mural decorations first found at Altamira, in the Cantabrian Pyrenees and at Marsoulas (Haute-Garonne). After these came the Portel in Ariège, the Tuc d'Audoubert, and the Trois-Frères on the estate of Count Begouën and his sons; Isturitz and Alquerdi in the Basque country; Montespan and Labastide in the central Pyrenees.

Caves and pot-holes and underground streams occur, as we have said before, both in the valleys and at moderate heights as well as near the higher summits. Quite recent discoveries among them call for some further description, and I venture to add a few details about finds I made when extending my researches and explorations in the main chain.

On the southern slopes behind the Cirque de Gavarnie in the Marboré massif, we found in 1926 the course of an underground river, which had become fossilized into a permanent natural ice cave. This cave, which passes right through the mountain, is at the exceptional height of nearly nine thousand feet; it is the highest ice cave known. It takes the form of an immense natural tunnel containing névé, frozen waterfalls, flat stretches of ice, and even an underground lake. This tunnel, where all is now frozen solid, was once the channel for a rushing subterranean torrent. The discovery of such a curious cavity, only separated from the Cirque de Gavarnie by the narrow crest of the frontier ridge, led the geologist Martel to put forward a theory as to the part played by erosion underground in the excavation of the Cirque; it was a hypothesis which had occurred to him long before and which had been hinted at by the naturalist Ramond as early as 1790. This view received the most fortunate confirmation in 1928 through a discovery by my late regretted colleague and friend Joseph Devaux, who perished at sea in the wreck of the *Pourquoi Pas*. He found in the upper tier of the Cirque a cavern containing an underground torrent which fed the great Cascade de Gavarnie, the source of the Gave de Pau.

Along a different line of thought I had been led to another curious conclusion which has received subsequent confirmation: the subterranean ice of the Marboré is fossilized. To gaze upon these glaciers under the earth which have never melted, these frozen lakes and rivers of everlasting ice, is an unforgettable and spellbinding experience. In the bowels of these great peaks, beneath these vaults whose utter silence fills the heart with awe, nature is frozen into immutability. Only a breath of icy air stirs in these lonely halls of silence, which no human eye has looked on for thousands of years and where none could dally and escape death.

The part played in the hollowing out of cirques in limestone mountains by water circulating below the surface seems to have received further confirmation from a series of fresh facts I have recently brought to light in the cirque of Le Haut-Lez in Ariège.

In exploring underground a torrent which we succeeded in following up for several miles in this cirque, we came to the foot of some waterfalls one above the other which tumbled into a vast hole, whose tiny outlet to the upper air was finally discovered at over seven thousand feet.

Vertical descents effected by long rope ladders beside these cascades enabled me to reach in this hole a depth of nearly a thousand feet. This huge chasm, hollowed out to a total depth of one thousand five hundred and eighty feet, is far the deepest in France and the fifth deepest in the world. This subterranean stream was missed when the neighbouring waters were utilized for a hydro-electric plant; it has now, as a result of my explorations, been captured and brought into use by means of a tunnel dug, in accordance with my directions, inside the mountain.

Another classic example of the remarkable behaviour of water underground high up in mountain country was afforded me when I was working on the identification of the principal source of the Garonne. In the final stages of this investigation, in which success was largely due to deductions based on geological knowledge, a costly and delicate experiment with colouring matter furnished con- clusive evidence that the source of the Garonne was on the southern slopes of the Pyrenees (the Mediterranean basin of the Ebro), where it disappears underground to pass under the axis of the chain by a tunnel deep below the surface and comes out again on the north side in the Val d'Aran before proceeding on its way to the Atlantic.

This experiment gave publicity to the results of three years' work, which solved a knotty problem in geography and hydrology; it also raised a curious point of international law, for Spain was preparing to divert into the Ebro the torrent in Aragon which we now know to be the infant Garonne. Now that the hydro-electric industry is rapidly increasing the production of water power in mountainous districts, it is time to insist on the growing interest of investigating underground streams, the nature of whose circulation and the control of whose use opens up a new and complicated subject.

The discovery of these mysterious watercourses, and in particular that of the Garonne, supports the very practical and in no way exceptional points I have summarized in the preceding pages. I need go no further than the examples already quoted to show that the opening up of these great recesses underground has brought new horizons into the field of view of geology and geography and even of international law.

But I cannot end these eulogies of the Pyrenean caves without a mention of the most famous, which every one must know, the one which was once the humble insignificant Grotto of Massabielle and is now known to the world as the Grotto of Lourdes. It is no small satisfaction to me in my role of Pyrenean explorer that the Virgin should have chosen a Pyrenean cave in which to manifest and extend her gifts.

Our trip through the cave country and past ages seems to have reached its end. It has certainly been a rapid and a shortened trip, we have done no more than cast hurried glances about us without attempting to go deeply into anything, and I am only too conscious that the great worldwide voyage, suitable to such a subject, has been a simple stroll. In the course of that stroll I have been irresistibly driven towards the region where I have been so happy.

I could not tear myself away and have had to stay and sing the praises of these Pyrenean caves.

I have some excuse, seeing that these cavities which I know so well are counted some of the richest in relics of man's distant past, and that they offer an incomparably varied field for exploration. I cannot end this chapter better than by quoting what I have written elsewhere: 'Where, indeed, can we experience such varied sensations, look upon such strange sights, live through moments so thrilling, so full of poetry; where can the joys of inward satisfaction be so keenly felt as among the surprises and the perils that await us when we go down into the recesses hidden far below the surface of the earth?

'If I have ventured to deal with prehistoric ages, it is because I have myself discovered strangely moving traces which have taken me back among the very scenes of the earliest stages of human life. As for geology, that terribly complex science, I have done no more than appreciate the depths of poetry it reveals and try occasionally to express in halting phrases the impression it has made on me.

'The savage charm of this underground world has, it seems to me, been little understood. A cave is not simply a place to inspire dread, ugly and desolate, not merely a void, a sort of grim menacing grimace on the face of nature. Many of the great halls I have gazed upon in wonder surpass in their majestic architecture the naves of the great cathedrals which excite our wonder and our admiration. And what infinite variety, what wonderful delicacy and purity there is in these formations of crystal, fashioned with elaborate care in the depths of the earth!

'Thoughts of the distant past come crowding into your mind as you stand in these hidden chambers into which our first ancestors groped their way, to perform ceremonies of a moving or a terrifying nature and to bury their dead. It is a thrilling experience to find, after the lapse of thousands of years, those touching evidences of their earliest attempts at artistic expression scraped upon the rock, their earliest weapons, their very bones, and even the print of their bare feet on the clay floor of the cave.

'Can you find anywhere better opportunities for quiet meditation or such an atmosphere of mystery as you do beneath the marble roofs of these temples built by nature, the scale of whose architecture so amazes us? It is true that light and life are banished from this underground world, but the solemn, overwhelming silence which reigns there and the memories of far distant ages that hover round you, give a ghostly life to these dark, lonely labyrinths below.'

2

THE UNDERGROUND WORLD

Regna solitudinis.

In my introduction to this book it was stated that its pages would be devoted mainly to my own personal observations and explorations. I find it difficult, and it would indeed be presumptuous on my part to present any survey of the underground regions if I confined my remarks to the caves of one particular district. It will therefore, I think, be useful to give a brief summary of what is known about the caves, pot-holes, and underground rivers in different parts of the world.

Man has traversed the earth in every direction, he has even flown over it. Every sea on its surface has been ploughed by his ships, every mountain chain is now known, and soundings have reached the deepest depths of the ocean. The era of great exploration on the surface of the earth has passed and little remains to be discovered and learned.

But what is below the surface is still to be explored, the secrets, hitherto inviolate, of countless caverns are waiting to reward their discoverers. Little is known about this underground world; men who would be ashamed not to know the name and height of a high peak, the name and length of a great river, or the position on the map of a small country or town, know nothing whatever about the chief aims and results of spelaeology. Most people know nothing of the world's biggest caves and deepest holes, neither their name nor size nor where they are.

To remedy this weakness in underground geography I hope a rapid survey of what has been done may be of help.

Such a survey may appear to offer rather dull reading,

but without giving figures it is difficult to present the information. It may be that some of these figures will not seem very impressive. Men's imaginations and their appetite for the marvellous have been too freely indulged in descriptions of caves, leading to a belief in their immense extent and their unfathomable depth.

The hurried round of visits I propose to make may destroy some existing tales and illusions, but it will, at any rate, give a fairly accurate general view; fairly accurate only, I repeat, because in the medley of vague or false information, and the exaggerations which are the general rule in such matters, it is difficult to give full and precise details. My readers may, I fear, be sometimes left without complete knowledge or complete certainty, deficiencies which, in these days, are almost unpardonable. At the start, then, I ask for all the indulgence you can allow me, for, as far as I know, this survey is the first of its kind, and a statistical statement about a region so shrouded in darkness must necessarily suffer from imperfections and omissions. And do not forget that no other domain of study is so little known as this underground world; it has only been studied and actively explored by a small number of spelaeologists for a bare half century.

Vast regions, whole continents indeed, are still un-surveyed, which shows how premature any statistics must be. I think there is enough known, however, to enable me to state the present position in this field of exploration.

Which is the biggest cave in the world? Undoubtedly the Mammoth Cave in the state of Kentucky, U.S.A., about eighty miles from Louisville. It is not called so because skeletons of mammoths have been found there, but simply because of its enormous size. It is to other caves what the mammoth was to other creatures of its time; it is the giant cave, the cave of mammoth dimensions.

As was stated in the previous chapter, it was discovered by a bear hunter in 1809 and it was a long time before the whole maze of underground cavities was catalogued.

Initial estimates greatly exaggerated the length, putting it at something like two hundred and twenty miles. After that there was a tendency to underestimate. To-day the avenues and chambers at various levels are believed to cover seventy miles or more. Meanwhile doubts exist, which it is not easy to clear away completely, because of peculiar difficulties in regard to this cave, quite apart from the physical obstructions to exploration. The authorities in charge of the cave have always opposed the making of any detailed or even of any general plan of it, and do not like the idea of any such document being brought to the surface.

It is obvious, in fact, that the labyrinths underground extend far beyond the limits of the society's property. The society is anxious to avoid any exercise of the rights conferred by the old legal adage, 'Every owner of the soil is owner of the subsoil.' Its neighbours might become rivals and create difficulties for the present exploiters of the cave and try to excavate on their own lands new artificial entrances to the cave, in order to start a rival business in its attractions. It is a regrettable situation from the scientists' point of view, for knowledge supplied by an accurate plan of the cave would be of great assistance in arriving at a better understanding of the working and development of the hydrogeological processes which have resulted in the formation of these tremendous cavities. Plan or no plan, the Mammoth Cave with its seventy miles of passages is certainly by far the biggest cave known.

Now there is little doubt that it communicates with several other caves by means of low-roofed or choked galleries which will, sooner or later, be cleared for access. The reasons given above are the only obstacles to this clearing of communications with the neighbouring caves known as Salts, White, Dixon, Long, Short, Crystal, Diamonds, Procter, etc. When the day of clearance comes, the whole collection of caves will probably cover at least a hundred and fifty miles.

É.-A. Martel, who spent three consecutive days in these caves, has given us his impression of these natural catacombs, the greatest in the world: 'What I felt in these caves was the monotonous, ceaseless impression of immensity they convey. As a manifestation of natural forces which have bored out and changed the whole appearance of the earth's rocky crust, we have here, without doubt, one of the most impressive phenomena to be seen on this planet of ours, on the same vast scale as the giant rivers of America, the falls of the Zambesi, of the Iguazu, and of Niagara, the volcanoes of the Andes or Hawaii, the glaciers of the Himalaya or the inland ice-cap of Greenland. But as a thing to look at with delight, as an example of those elegant or majestic works of beauty produced by the fanciful growths of stalactite and stalagmite, the Mammoth Cave bears simply no comparison with the wonders of the French caves of Aven Armand, Padirac, Dargilau, etc.

'At the same time, some of its galleries are of colossal dimensions exceeding the most majestic examples at Lombrive, Niaux, Sabart in Ariège, at Adelsberg in Carniola, at Agtelek in Hungary, and at Han-sur-Lesse. And the numerous chasms inside, with their rugged coverings of calcite, would be a splendid sight if the soot from torches had not blackened those that are easiest to see; you have to go as far as those of Hovey's Cathedral to see their original natural splendour. The finest of all the sights of the Mammoth Cave is there. I consider it one of the most striking things I have ever seen underground.'

Next in order of size on our list of greatest caves must certainly come another American cave, the Carlsbad Cavern in Texas, discovered in 1901. But there is a tiresome doubt as to the dimensions to be attributed to this cave, which the Government has lately declared a national park. An odd system of measurement has been adopted and the area explored estimated at about nine hundred and thirty acres. As regards the total length of the galleries widely differing estimates have been arrived at. It looks as if a figure of thirty miles might be accepted for the time being, while the exploration of the cave is incomplete.

Other American caves, Wind Cave, Oregon Cave, Jeswell, etc., seem to be of immense size, but no accurate details are available.

If the dimensions of American caves are still only known approximately, that is not at all the case with those of Europe, which have been surveyed with completely satisfying accuracy. The largest of them is in the Austrian Alps, not far from Salzburg. In a mountain formation there rich in caves, there are more than four hundred, the most important being the Eisriesenwelt (the World of Ice Giants). It is at a height of 5,600 feet and presented its explorers from 1913 to 1930 with a maze of passages eighteen miles in length, one and a quarter miles of which are partly filled with ice formations of great size.

The old Austrian cave of Adelsberg (renamed Postumia since its annexation by Italy in 1920), thanks to the cutting of artificial tunnels which link it up with several other caves (Planina, Piuca, Paradiso), now attains a total length of fourteen and a half miles. Though the existence of the cave was known as early as the eighteenth century, no systematic attempt was made to explore it till about 1830. It has been made extremely easy of access, and its attractions now include a concert hall, an electric railway, a spelaeological museum, and science laboratories.

The cave of Agtelek in Hungary and the Domitsa cave in Slovakia share an underground river, 'the Styx,' and have natural means of communication with each other, and together they extend for over eleven miles. This example of a natural communication between two countries underground must be rare; it was discovered in 1930.

After Agtelek-Domitsa there is a considerable drop in size, and several caves only attain some six or seven miles. Among the best known I mention the ice cave of the Dachstein in Austria, just over eight miles, and the Höll-Loch or Trou d'Enfer in Switzerland. Both of these made extraordinary demands on the courage and skill of the explorers. At the Höll-Loch, in particular, floods may devastate the cave and constitute a formidable danger.

A great many caves from three to six miles in length occur in different parts of the world; in the absence of exact information the only ones I shall mention before I come to the caves of France are those of Cacahuamilpa in Mexico, Lapa de Brejoin in Brazil (nearly four miles), the Lur-Loch in Styria, and Han-sur-Lesse in Belgium (three miles).

In France our biggest cavity is the underground river of Bramabiau in Gard, partially explored in 1888 by Martel and his assistants for a distance of one and a quarter miles. Subsequently one of our pioneers in spelaeology, Félix Mazauric, undertook the systematic exploration of a labyrinth of galleries adjoining the river which have a total length of four and a half miles. De Lapierre has recently carried out further explorations which have brought the total length to over six miles.

Among other great caves in France I should mention that of Miremont in Dordogne, over three miles long. This cave has been known for two hundred years; it is lacking in picturesque and interesting details and is, in fact, one of the caves that have no columns, stalactites, or stalagmites; it is just a tunnel hollowed out of chalk.

The Côte Patière in Ardèche is a long cave which is dangerous to visit because of the floods which periodically sweep through it. It was explored for a distance of one and a quarter miles by Gaupillat in 1892. Two spelaeologists, de Joly and Dujardin-Weber more than doubled this by further exploration in 1937.

The Great Vent of Rognes in Gard, a gallery two and a half miles long, was explored in 1936 by a party of thirteen, partly French, partly Swiss, led by de Joly and Vesinet.

Bétharram in Basses-Pyrénées, two and a quarter miles long, is of vast proportions. Access to this cave has been made easy, and parts of the four levels that have so far been explored are visited by thousands of tourists every year. It was discovered in 1850, and the investigation of the lower reaches was undertaken in 1896–8 by three Pyrenean enthusiasts from Pau, Lary, Campan, and Ritter.

Various spelaeologists have explored the underground river of Labouiche in Ariège since 1908. Part of it was made accessible to tourists in 1938; the total length is nearly two and a quarter miles.

The cave of La Cigalère in Ariège is an underground torrent course nearly two miles long, explored by me in 1931. Communication between this cave and the great Martel Hole, of which it forms a lower storey, is by a series of waterfalls from thirty to sixty feet in height; nine of these have been ascended, though their ascent presented serious difficulties.

The Lombrive cave in Ariège has been long known because of its great towering entrance and its imposing galleries. The Spéléo-Club of Aude under Dr. Cannac has recently carried the exploration of this cave to a distance of nearly two miles.

Then come a number of caves of round about one and a half miles; Trabuc in Gard, Niaux in Ariège, Padirac in Lot, Saint-Marcel-d'Ardèche in Ardèche, Les Cavoittes in Jura, the Trou du Glaz, etc. Some of these are very fine indeed, but still not the finest in France. I cannot, in any case, attempt to give the name or description of every French cave.

Returning to our rapid survey of the world's cavities, I shall say something of the deepest chasms known. Compared with the miles of length of the greatest caves, the hundreds of feet of depth reached in underground chasms may make a poor showing; all the same, the exploration of these vertical shafts is, as a rule, a far more difficult and hazardous affair than that of caves. Such descents are made much less often, and the classification of these deep holes—though it needs constant revision—is more accurately established than that of caves. The reason is that

SEMI-TRANSPARENT DRAPERY

WALL ORNAMENTS OF GYPSUM

the possible sources of error in measurement are much
reduced, such measurements being usually arrived at by
soundings or by the amount of ropes and ladders
used.

Italy possesses the two deepest pot-holes: the chasm of
La Preta in Mont Lessini in the province of Verona, which
is 2,090 feet deep, and the Mouth of Aeolus or cave of
Corchia in the Apuan Alps of Tuscany, which is 1,835 feet.
Next to these comes the Austrian hole of Tonion in the
Styrian Alps; it has been explored to a depth of 1,730 feet
and soundings have been taken to 1,830 feet. The hole
of Verco in Gorizia province is 1,700 feet. Italy also holds
the fifth place with the chasm of Montenero in Carniola
with a depth of 1,575 feet. The other chasms of over
1,300 feet are also in Italy: Bertarelli in Istria, 1,475 feet,
Prez and Clana, 1,380 feet. After these about fifty holes
from 1,300 to 800 feet deep.

France has the Martel pot-hole in Ariège, which I
explored to a depth of nearly 1,000 feet by its upper
opening and a further 500 feet by ascending inside its
lower storey, known as the cave of La Cigalière. The
unexplored interval between is impenetrable owing to its
narrowness and is only a few yards in length; the total
difference of level between top and bottom is 1,580 feet.

The next deepest French chasm is that of Heyle or the
Puits d'Audiette in Basses-Pyrénées. Here Max Cosyns
and Vander Elst reached a depth of 800 feet. In the
Trou du Glaz in Isère P. Chevalier with nine companions
descended 735 feet below the surface opening.

Then come three chasms explored by the Spéléo-Club
of Paris: the 'chourum' of the Combe de Fer in Isère,
710 feet; the 'chourum' Dupont in Dévoluy, 707 feet;
and the hole of La Luire in Vercors, 697 feet.

Le Paradis in Doubs and the Aven de Hures in Lozère
end the list of French chasms of more than 650 feet; the
former was explored by the Paris Spéléo-Club, the latter
by Robert de Joly.

H

In America, Asia, and Oceania, no chasms have yet been found much over 300 feet deep. In Africa I discovered and explored the pot-hole of Frugato (623 feet), and that of Kef el Sao (472 feet) in the Moroccan Atlas. These are, at present, the deepest known in Africa.

Knowing now the maximum dimensions of caves and pot-holes, the reader may be astonished to find that, except in the case of the vast caves of the U.S.A., these underground regions are not on a bigger scale, and he may be tempted to compare them with the works carried out by man, who has excavated miles of galleries and shafts of 3,000 to 6,000 feet in depth in his mines.

These works are indeed wonderful, but it would be unfair and out of place to try to establish a parallel between the facilities of access to these artificially made caves (where one goes about in a trolley or a lift) and the natural obstacles offering formidable difficulties which are the general rule in the case of natural caves. There are some cave exploration enterprises which have been pursued by successive generations of workers and are still going on. For thirty years advance has been continuing in the terrible ice caves of the Eisriesenwelt; and it has taken several years to overcome the difficulties presented by the great Italian chasms. For, in this exploration underground, everything becomes singularly more difficult.

A darkness that is total and never ends, tunnels that become narrowed or blocked, steep climbs, showers of stones, rock-falls, poisonous gases, a perpetual, penetrating damp, mud, icy water, unforeseen floods of devastating volume, breakages in the apparatus, the risk of losing the way in the labyrinth of passages, accidents whose consequences are vastly more serious underground: all these things forbid any comparison of artificially made excavations with the formidable caverns hollowed out by nature.

I need not dwell further on the obvious differences, but will proceed, without any claim that my list is complete, or its details rigorously exact, to give a few additional facts and pictures which may help to make this cave world better known.

The most spacious of subterranean halls is that of the Giant Cave near Trieste. In size it far surpasses any effort of human architecture, measuring 787 feet by 433 feet, and its ceiling goes up to 452 feet. The huge mass of St. Peter's in Rome, including its dome, could be put inside it.

In the Vent of Fouillac (Hérault), my colleague the Abbé Gitry has found a hall 490 feet by 270 feet with a ceiling reaching 150 feet. At La Rocca di San Canzian (Italy), and also at Padirac (Lot), there are ceilings nearly 300 feet high. In the chasm of La Légarde (Doubs) there is a chamber 330 feet by 165 feet and 425 feet high. The portal which gives access to the Grotte de Bournillon in Dauphiné is 330 feet high. The great dome of the Grotte de Han-sur-Lesse (Belgium), and the Hall of the Cross in the Grotto of Postumia are on a like majestic scale. In the vast Eisriesenwelt, the great Mörk chamber, in which is the urn containing the ashes of the explorer Mörk, is 165 feet high.

In the deep chasms, which are usually formed by a succession of shafts, sensational vertical drops occur. The giant of the species is that of the Enrico Revel (Italy); there the explorers had to unroll their apparatus and descend a vertical shaft which drops without a break for 1,035 feet. In the chasms of La Bainsizza and Lipizza (Trieste) the sheer drops are 935 feet and 680 feet. In France several vents and pot-holes necessitate sheer descents of between 500 and 600 feet.

The formations of carbonate of lime (stalactites, stalagmites, wall decorations) sometimes reach remarkable dimensions in caves. These 'monuments' are generally of very great beauty and have taken thousands of years to construct. Though it is particularly ungracious to classify natural beauties like these according to their size, I will mention that the finest and tallest stalactites known are those in the Armand chasm in Lozère. They form a cluster of 400 columns of entrancing beauty, many of them 60 or 70 feet high, the tallest 100 feet. 'It is quite impossible,' writes É.-A. Martel, 'to describe this collection of trees made of carbonate of lime, cypresses of stone, which has been named *Forêt vierge* and is, in truth, the "apotheosis of caverns." No other cave in the world contains anything like it; it is one of the luckiest finds ever made underground.' Among other remarkable constructions of lime I must mention the *Monument* du Caougno de las Gouffios (Ariège) which is over 80 feet, the Astronomical Tower in the Dargilan cave in Lozère, the Ship and the Giant Pillars in the chasm of Orgnac in Ardèche, etc.

More than anything else underground the lakes found there have stirred the imagination and given rise to the strangest exaggerations. People still talk of underground lakes, of huge, deep, inexhaustible expanses of water. No doubt prodigious reserves of water of limitless extent do exist in the depths of the earth, but these supposed sheets of water are only phreatic, i.e., waters which impregnate more or less permeable soils. Actual large pockets of water imprisoned underground exist mainly in the mind's eye and are, in any case, of extremely rare occurrence. There are no free stretches of water on which one can sail about, certainly such lakes are much smaller affairs than is generally believed. I say quite definitely, though it may be destroying a cherished illusion, that no underground lake has yet been discovered which is more than 90 yards across. As for the lakes supposed to be more than 100 yards long which are referred to in some explorers' descriptions, they are nothing more than widenings of rivers. The dislocation and cleavage of rocks tend to prevent the formation of extensive sheets of water. The Martel Lake in the Dragons' Cave in Majorca, the Lake of Padirac and that of Han, the Black Lake, now dried up in the

A SPRAY OF GYPSUM

A STALAGMITE

Eisriesenwelt, are no exceptions to the rule stated above. The lake in the chasm of Mazocha in Moravia has an exceptional dimension exceeding 100 yards, but it is 100 yards in depth.

Underground streams, on the other hand, are very numerous and often of imposing dimensions. It is what one would expect, since, except for a few hollows due to freaks of construction in the earth's crust, all caves and deep chasms have been excavated and modified through having been—as in many cases they still are—the channels of waters circulating in the fissures and pre-existing faults of limestone rocks. Many of these underground streams have been explored for several miles, but the roofs of the caves in which they flow sink and form submerged roofs or *siphons*, which are most formidable obstacles to any further exploration.

Among such streams there is a type which, after flowing along on the surface, disappears underground through openings or entrances to caves to which access is generally possible. These streams may disappear without reappearing or, at any rate, without any 'rising' being known. On the other hand, risings exist whose place of origin or disappearance is unknown. This is the case with large risings, which proceed, as a rule, from general infiltrations of water over an extensive area. The flow of water underground is an important chapter of hydrogeology, and these subterranean water systems offer all the special features of surface rivers: waterfalls, tributary streams, divisions, flooding, drying up, erosion, etc.

Among the underground rivers which are navigable, or at least capable of being followed over certain stretches, may be mentioned: the Pinka, the Timavo, the Recca in Italy; the Mazocha-Punkwa in Moravia; and in France the rivers of Padirac, Bétharram, and Labouiche, frequently visited by tourists. But the greatest underground river in the world is that of Trebinjčica in Herzogovina, which finally emerges into the light of day at the Ombla of Ragusa after five stretches underground, whose total length is over sixty miles.

Many other subterranean rivers exist whose points of disappearance and reappearance are known, but which it has hitherto been impossible to enter and explore. That is the case with the Garonne between the hole called the Trou du Toro and the Goueil de Jouéou (the Eye of Jove), and also with the communicating stream between the Danube and the Aach, which is a tributary of the Rhine, and in other cases.

One more question I will try to deal with: Which is the most potent rising in the world? Supremacy in such a case is almost impossible to establish, for the whole system of water circulation underground is subject to seasonal variations; moreover, the emerging flood is often flowing in a very uneven bed, making it practically impossible to gauge or even estimate the rate of flow. It is obvious, however, that some of these resurgent streams attain an impressive output of water. In the U.S.A. there are many risings with an output of 4,000 to 5,000 gallons per second, the Timavo in Italy gives over 5,300 gallons, the Ombla of Ragusa 3,750 gallons. In France the celebrated Fontaine de Vaucluse varies from under 2,000 to over 35,000 gallons; it is probably the greatest rising in the world. La Touvre near Angoulême is the next largest in France. Other large risings are Fontaine-l'Évêque in Var, La Sorgue d'Aveyron in Aveyron, La Fontaine Divonne at Cahors, La Loue in Doubs, Le Loiret, La Fou in Hérault, etc.

You will see that the underground world offers many subjects of interest, though I have not attempted to give more than a hasty and imperfect summary. My object has been simply to offer a temporary, provisional list and to give some definite information about the dimensions and the characteristic features of caves and pot-holes and underground rivers.

The regions below the surface are still little known

and much is conjectural, but they promise rich rewards and discoveries to future explorers. What a field of exploration is here, and what vast portions of this underground world remain unknown in the impenetrable bowels of the earth!

3

THE EXPLORER'S EQUIPMENT

Objets inanimés, avez-vous donc une âme . . .?
LAMARTINE, *Le Lac.*

I had occasion to dedicate a former work of mine 'To my children and all young Frenchmen to foster a love of underground France.' Nothing has given me more encouragement than the letters I have had from young people, telling me how reading about my cave campaigns has attracted them to the world below, and how their first attempts have made them convinced enthusiasts. Of all the satisfactions that can come to a writer who describes what he feels and what has captured his affections, there is none better than that of having evoked an echo, a feeling of shared enthusiasm, or even of having aroused a longing to pursue a similar end in some reader who takes the trouble to let him know of it.

The tributes of this kind which I have appreciated most of all are letters from children. One small boy, in a scrawl not exempt from misspellings, announces he wants to learn geology with a view to becoming a cave explorer and says he already possesses a geological hammer! A small coquette, writing on fancy paper, wants to know 'in what caves she can find cave pearls to make herself a fine necklace.' Another more seriously minded child would like to add to her insect collection some cave beetles, and confesses her fears and difficulties, never having ventured into any cave.

And one can hardly fail to be touched by the letters that sometimes arrive from distant countries and from the pens of widely different types of persons. A colonist, living alone in the Australian bush, where he has been a stock-farmer for twenty years, tells in most moving terms the nostalgia my descriptions awakened in him for the caves of his native Switzerland which he had begun to explore as a lad. A Polish nun felt the appeal of the solitudes below, which reached her only through my books, for she had never even seen a cave. From a foreign geologist who led a scientific expedition to the Caucasus comes an enthusiastic letter with a photograph of a high peak previously unnamed for which his party were kind enough to suggest my name.

Along with these letters come others of a practical nature, requests for information from engineers who have been asked to carry out exceptional kinds of work in caves; from sportsmen attracted by the difficulties of certain types of exploration; from scouts anxious to be initiated in the practical side of spelaeology, who ask innumerable questions; from landowners and industrialists wanting to have a water supply on their property; from bodies interested in attracting tourists hoping to find in their locality picturesque caves which could be made accessible and exploited.

Other letters are quite disinterested and full of touching anxiety for my safety; they are apt to be rather naïve and occasionally somewhat presuming. One old lady begs me to be careful and to guard against chills. A retired gendarme cannot understand why I carry no arms when I go underground, and after listing the various weapons which might ensure my safety, he urges me to provide myself with a dagger! A schoolmistress points out quite plainly and with arguments whose nature can easily be guessed, though their validity is a matter of opinion, that a family man has no business to turn explorer. Not having the address of this particular correspondent I could not justify myself by pointing out that my vocation of explorer came to me twenty years before marriage. I cannot see that the fact of my home having been five times blessed with a new arrival is any more incompatible with my calling than in the case of an air pilot, a miner, a sailor, a tiler, or . . . a pedestrian in Paris!

And to end my list there are many correspondents who are good enough to tell me of caves which they believe to be unexplored or of special interest. Beside these items of information, which can be quite valuable, I could mention some sent by inventors recommending their own special methods or apparatus, mainly in regard to lighting and vertical descents in deep holes, and above all to the question of making the air in caves fit to breathe, a point which seems to worry a great many people. In this connection various kinds of oxygen apparatus have been brought to my notice as a precaution against the deadly carbonic acid gas. A female chemistry student has advised me always to keep about me a bit of oxylith, and to moisten it at the slightest warning of danger, to make it give off a reviving flow of oxygen. In order to detect in time the presence of noxious gases a country vicar recommends a method he says is infallible (it is so, in fact, and was formerly used in certain mines, but would hardly be practicable) which consists in taking down a small live bird in a cage!

The Corporation des Radiesthésistes occasionally honours me with its interest, and several diviners with the pendulum have offered their services and notified me of caves, which have, unfortunately, no known communication with the outer world; a thing to make a spelaeologist suffer agonies of frustration. I have not felt it my duty to send maps or photographs of localities to various water diviners who asked for them, and claimed to be able to detect at a distance, merely from such documents, the existence and location of caves hitherto unknown. But I agreed to have a try out with one of them, who wanted to check his powers by an attempt to trace, far from the actual spot, on a large-scale map, the plan of underground caves with which I was quite familiar. Such a try out was above suspicion and the results could be checked. Truth, however, compels me to say that the plans drawn from the indications of the pendulum were as far as they could be from according

with reality. On the other hand, prospecting on the spot
with the divining twig or the pendulum appears to give
sometimes definitely useful results, and I would be the last
to deny that there is in certain people a kind of water sense;
for I have, with my own eyes, seen the twig break in my
mother's hands when she crossed, without knowing it, the
underground channel of the Garonne.

Turning now to another line of thought about caves,
there is a belief in treasure hidden in them that is widespread and dies very hard.   It is a chapter that has no end,
and the greatest part of the correspondence I get deals with
this subject.   I apologize for the space I am giving to it,
but a few brief comments may be of interest.   Many dis-
creet and mysterious letters are addressed to me by people
who suspect or say they know of treasure lying in the
depths of caves, and as they have not the courage to explore
them alone, they propose to go halves in the booty with the
explorer!

One old doctor wrote me nine letters entreating me to
go and explore a cave in the Var, which he had not
seen since he was a child.   Certain documents in his
possession made him quite certain there was hidden treasure
there.   One day I happened to be in that neighbourhood,
and being anxious to show my willingness to help, even if
I failed to give him what he wanted, I made inquiries about
this cave of his.   But despite the extraordinarily detailed
indications in his letter, no one on the spot was aware of
the mere existence of such a cave.   This particular correspondent, odd as he is, is by means exceptional, far from it;
the mysterious nature of the world below seems to stir into
special activity the imaginations of these visionaries who
write me such astounding letters.

An American astrologer (a Humanitarian Harmonist)
described on his letter paper as 'the Revealer of the five
planets beyond Neptune, whose times of revolution round
the sun vary from 228 to 3,600 years, the said planets
being unknown to Astronomy and Science,' sends me a

horoscope from the cave of Montespan where I discovered in 1923 important evidences of prehistoric man.   It is a verbose and fantastic horoscope beginning with this sentence, by no means the oddest in this weird scrawl: 'In 19498 B.C. exactly on the 26th December (!), a tribe which had been living in the mountains of northern Europe,' etc.

A Frenchman who lives in Paraguay and hopes to return one day to France suggested that he and I should co-operate in a vast project which was to consist, among other things, in making 'a complete telestereoscopic survey of points on the horizon from a certain mountain he knew of, in order that from a comparison of the results there might emerge a great law or fact which would have an immense scientific and practical value for statesmen, politicians, the public weal, engineers, even for county councils or smaller local authorities. . . .'

A retired cavalry major has sent me an interminable dissertation on the prehistoric caves of France; it is a manuscript in close small writing, which contains neither paragraphs nor stops, not so much as a comma; an eight-page sentence!   Then there is a Dutchman, who seems to think I have discovered a salt lake underground.   According to him such a lake is bound to contain iodine.   He happens to know of an extremely cheap method of extracting the iodine, and suggests a lucrative combine in which all the conditions and the smallest details of the undertaking are carefully thought out, except, of course, the existence of the famous lake!

I must also mention the colonist in Morocco—he may be pulling my leg—who has seen hundreds of pot-holes on the grand scale, but still unexplored, in the Apennines. His letter ends with a PS. (*in cauda venenum*), which reveals that he is talking of the Apennines in the moon and that all his exploring has been done sitting at his telescope!

My list shall end with the misunderstood and persistent musician who would like to have subterranean echoes

FLOWERS OF THE UNDERGROUND WORLD

FLOWERS OF GYPSUM FROM THE CAVE OF
LA CIGALÈRE, ARIÈGE

recorded by phonograph or wireless and who has hitherto failed to interest public authorities in the scheme.

With apologies for devoting so much space to these letters, varied as they are, amusing, pathetic, naïve, emotional or practical, quaint, absurd, pitiful, let us come to the serious subject of this chapter.

As I have said, requests pour in for information as to the best kind of clothes to wear, the apparatus to be carried, how to light the way underground. This being so, it seems desirable to devote a chapter to a description of the outfit needed by a spelaeologist. Having no desire to compile a detailed catalogue and still less to write the perfect spelaeologist's handbook, I will compromise by inviting my readers to note down the items of my own equipment, such as it is, with any advantages it may have, as well as the inevitable omissions and defects it must contain; for it makes no claim to perfection, it is just the outcome of my own personal views on the best methods of exploring underground.

It would certainly have been a skilful and more attractive way of describing the necessary equipment, to take the items one by one and illustrate their use in the course of a particular bit of exploration, but one never carries or uses all of them at the same time. And so, to give you a true picture, I shall introduce you to my outfit where it lies when not in use, up in the attic under the roof, a lonely part of the house to which stealthy visits are paid only when I leave on an expedition or return from one. On this occasion, since a detailed inspection is due, the darkness which usually reigns shall be banished by raising the trap-door which opens to the sky. We shall then be able to make our inventory in the dazzling light reflected from the whitewashed walls. Before we go in and begin to rummage in the strange collection of lumber there, I will ask you to pause for a moment while I try and recall something of my own early efforts.

When I answer the many letters I get containing all

sorts of questions on the practical side of spelaeology, I always advocate simplicity and economy. When I go back to my start as an explorer I am reminded that my first prospecting was remarkable for the precarious nature of my lighting arrangements, for a complete absence of equipment and apparatus and, I may add, a complete absence of clothing. For several years my explorations were carried out by the flickering light of candles held in the hand, with nothing to guide me beyond a sort of cave sense and in an Adamesque costume which even the cave-men themselves, dressed in the skins of beasts, would have considered somewhat scanty.

Nowadays I should never dream of embarking on explorations of any importance with such an inadequate light, with bare feet, and on my head a waterproof cap to keep my matches dry, and with nothing on but a rope slung round me to help me over the steepest places.

While I do not for a moment justify or recommend such a scanty and primitive outfit as this (though it did not prevent my doing bits of exploration which led to some important discoveries), I must utter a word of warning against going to the opposite extreme. Burdening themselves with a heavy, complicated lot of implements is often the undoing of beginners who want to have with them a comprehensive outfit containing tools suitable for any obstruction and any of the frequent emergencies that occur in cave work. The results can be deplorable; the enthusiasm of a beginner, paralysed and exhausted by the intolerable burden he carries, gives place to a disillusionment that may put him off spelaeology for good. I could name two men, one a great mountaineer, the other the hero of a thrilling adventure on the sea, who joined a cave exploring party that was heavily overloaded, and gave up any further thought of such a sport, deeming it beyond their powers and also devoid of any sort of attraction.

Another question, very different from that of overladen and too numerous parties, is that of solitary exploration

underground. One writer on the subject—not himself a
solitary explorer—regards it as admissible in certain cases,
provided the individual is possessed of 'a perfectly cool
head, complete self-control, and an incredible amount of
guts.' For my own part, I have often been underground alone and my experience leaves me in no doubt at
all; if mountaineering and sailing alone are universally
discouraged, and moreover seldom practised, spelaeology
under those conditions is unquestionably more trying and
more dangerous and should be condemned. Devoted as I
am to this type of exploration and the occasionally excessive
excitements it gives, I can in no case advise any one to
venture alone into the dark labyrinths that exist below.
Contrary to all logic and my own example I must here cry
mea culpa, and tell you: 'Do what I say and don't do what
I do,' except at your own risk and peril! There are not
likely to be many infringements of the prohibition, but I
wanted to state it emphatically in order to clear myself of
any responsibility in the matter.

That ends this somewhat long digression and brings me
back to the entrance to my attic, that is to say, my cloak-
room, lamp-room, and tool-house all in one, where we will
first have a look at the dress department.

COSTUME

Here, in a corner, hanging on a coat-rack is my working
costume: cloth trousers of the type adopted by skiers, that
is to say, with narrowing ends provided with elastic straps
to go under the foot and fit into the top of the boot. None
of your ordinary trousers with loose ends that may catch in
things or gape open unpleasantly, ruck up and bare the
legs at the least effort or pull on them. None of your
breeches either that fit tight at the knee or have a strap
that presses on the back of it and are usually worn with
fancy-topped stockings; no nasty stiff leather gaiters or

puttees that come undone at awkward moments and compress the calves when they get wet.

The second item in my costume is this stout linen blouse with zip fastening running all the way up, thus doing away with buttons which are frequently torn off and can be extremely painful in the throes of reptation. The advantage of the blouse is that it does not involve, as jackets do, superfluous flaps or tails, with the added drawbacks of pockets and bands which add to one's bulkiness and are a serious hindrance to progress in places where the utmost slimness is required. And lastly this very roomy attachment of the sleeve allows much more freedom of movement to the arms and shoulders than the ordinary sleeve fitted close up to the jacket.

Over this comfortable and, to my mind, quite becoming costume you have to draw the most inelegant old rag, patched in several places, that hangs limply on a nail in the wall. I call it my *salopette*, the linen overall, whose praises have been already sung in the chapter on reptation. This shapeless garment for purely working purposes with clay stains all over it—too frequent washings would remove the surfacing and make the stuff too pliable—is the armour I wear against wet and mud; it protects the clothes from direct contact with the rocks and, being made in one piece, it diminishes the chances of being caught up and wedged. The elbows and knees are strengthened with extra pieces of stuff, so that it survives for a considerable time the constant wear and terrible chafing of the rocks, but it is not a garment to attract the fastidious, for it makes those who put it on look like anthropoid apes or plantigrades, with a slight suggestion of the porker that has been rolling in the mud! There are forms of sport which enjoy favour because of the attractive dress or undress appropriate to them; spelaeology is a muddy sport, without elegance and without any admiring gallery, and it is unlikely to find many adherents among the ladies. I remember emerging one day from a particularly filthy shaft in front of a very elegant

THE RUBBER BOAT

SURVEYING
UNDERGROUND

crowd of sightseers, the scene of my operations being close
to a watering-place, and being greeted as I came into the
light of day by such a chorus of horrified cries and pretence
of fright that I quite forgot the demands of self-restraint
and courtesy, the onlookers being mainly women.

Standing on the top rungs of my ladder, a revolting
object even to those who had been helping my ascent, I
raised a hand with slime dripping from it and holding a
great block of mud which could no longer be called a
helmet, and parodying the immortal phrase Rostand puts
into the mouth of his 'cadet de Gascogne,' I bowed to the
assembled company and announced with an emphasis that
implied its application to myself alone: 'Moi, c'est morale-
ment que j'ai mon élégance!'

FOOTWEAR

Now we come to the boots, the lowliest of my servants, harder worked even than my overall, and like it
needing frequent renewal. They are stowed away on the
floor in a corner after being washed all over after use and
dried in the shade.

The usage they have to endure is terribly destructive;
the soles are slashed by sharp rocks, there is very heavy
wear and tear on the uppers and ends when backing up
chimneys or worming one's way forward at full length,
there are long immersions in water and mud; it would be a
pity to buy or have made high quality stuff. Just common
boots such as the army wears will be quite adequate. The
boots are well nailed but not like those of climbers for ice-
work. Special types of nails like *tricounis* or wing nails are
to be rejected; otherwise you will find pounds and pounds
of sticky clay picked up with every step of either foot.
Moreover, this type of nailing would be a nuisance and
needlessly heavy on the many occasions of going up or
down rope ladders. The laces should go through holes and
not over hooks, a small but important point to remember,

I

otherwise you would be constantly getting caught up on the fine steel ropes at the sides of the ladders, a tiring and dangerous thing for the explorer and very bad for the ladders themselves, which can be severely damaged by this shearing.

It would be no good trying to get waterproof soles and uppers, and folding sewn-in tongues will be useless, since it is often necessary to walk or swim in the water, and no boot remains watertight in such conditions. One lucky day I found some boots with holes in them, for exploring some caves with streams running through them. They had the distinct advantage over new boots of emptying immediately after each immersion.

My rather light-hearted treatment of the boot question may be due to my having been much addicted to going barefoot. In fact, all the barefoot school not only disdain the use of boots, but do not easily get used to enclosing their feet in these leather cases, which annoy them and hurt them far more than the unevennesses of the ground.

When I was exploring the holes and caves of the Atlas Mountains, I advised my Chleuh porters to wear boots to guard against possible infection in any cuts they got from contact with the dead creatures lying on the floor. However, they preferred their *souliers de baptême*, as they were humorously described to André Martignon, the author of *Montagne*, by a Pyrenean shepherd immensely proud of the horny soles of his feet.

The Helmet

My metal helmet, on the other hand, was most willingly accepted by these same primitive porters as a protection against showers of stones. Here it is, reposing on a ledge, next my wife's; as you see, it is just an ordinary army Adrian helmet. I do not pretend it is an ideal one for a spelaeologist, and headwear of expanded rubber or duralumin would be better; but I am a person of habit and prejudice in my methods of equipment, and my preference for the old trench helmet is a matter of sentiment. Ever since 1915 when it covered my close-cropped head, when I was a 'bluebottle' of eighteen, it has been in service. Its many dints bear witness to the innumerable and mostly unnoticed knocks it has had; though some of them tell a story which is a secret between it and me; they take us from Champagne and Verdun to my adventures underground in Africa and the Pyrenees. The most obvious of the bumps was produced in the great hole of Boucou in the Haute-Garonne as the result of a fall of more than three hundred feet, in which luckily only the helmet was involved; I myself was left clinging desperately to the ladder.

When the matter which had occasioned our sudden divorce was settled and I could follow my helmet to the bottom of the hole, I found my poor friend had a grievous wound; also the leather lining had been torn away from the outer cover, and from between the two I picked out a carefully folded bit of paper, which I proceeded to decipher with amazement. And who would not have been amazed to find and read in 1936 at the bottom of a hole in the Pyrenees a page from the *Bulletin des Armées de la République*, dated August 1916? It took me a moment to realize that the extraordinary fall which had torn off the crest and entirely removed the lining had also jerked out the paper which I had one day in the trenches inserted between the steel and the leather, because my helmet was too big. The incident was a reminder that the helmet had remained 'undemobilized' ever since, and that is why I cannot bear to part with it. May I still be able to wear it when I am turning grey, even hoary, about the temples!

In addition to these accidental changes of form, this helmet of mine has suffered others which might be called professional. The badge in front, for example, the famous grenade with its embossed tongue of fire, has been replaced by another flame, a sort of electric lamp, with a nickel

reflector.   Instead of the regulation leather chin-strap with
its rather clumsy buckle, it now has two rubber straps, one
for the chin, one for the back of the neck; this double safeguard enables the helmet to be put on firmly and quickly,
except when some particularly odd and unforeseen acrobatics are necessary, which I admit can happen in the course
of my explorations.

The wearing of a helmet on long and formidable descents
of deep holes gives a feeling of security against the terrible
stone-falls which are one of the greatest dangers in cave
work.   The security may be more imagined than actual.
When the rain of stones is caused by the friction of the
lowering gear against the sides, while the explorer is
hanging on to the ladders, the instantaneous instinctive
reaction which makes him press his head into his shoulders
and get close up against the ladder is better than any
theoretical defence.   In this position many of the missiles
will be diverted by hitting the sides or rungs, the helmet
will be a protection if the stones are not too big and have
not acquired too great a velocity.   In short, one may say
that while the helmet is of no avail against an avalanche of
rocks, it is very efficacious against showers of stones.   And
in regard to bumps against the walls as you swing on the
ladder, or the occasional collisions between your head
and ceilings that are low or studded with stalactites, the
protection is complete and saves you from many a wound.

There is one other small point, but a very necessary
one, that I should mention.   If you have to consult your
compass with the helmet on, be careful not to bend your
head too low, for fear of deflecting the needle.   If this
happens it is always tiresome, and in some cases it may
have serious consequences.

Gloves

Beside my helmet lies the last item in my wardrobe,
leather gloves like gardening gloves.   They are a nice

addition, but not essential to the outfit, though at times
extremely useful.

With these gloves for cave work, you need to choose a
size larger than for town use; they are of sheepskin, neither
too thick nor too thin and, of course, never fur-lined,
easily put on and taken off, and they leave complete freedom
of movement to the fingers and have no button fastening.

For climbing a smooth rope and, as a rule, in rock-
climbing, it is best not to wear gloves; it may even be
dangerous to do so.   But on certain occasions they are a
most efficient and acceptable protection against mud or
walls with crystals or other sharp projections on them.
Without them, it may be quite impossible to keep the
hands clean enough to take notes or make a rough plan of
a cave, for with bare hands the clay sticks to the fingers
like glue, making a sort of web between them.   The
greatest value of gloves, however, is the protection they
give against cuts and scratches to which the bare hands
are inevitably exposed, and particularly in preventing these
slight wounds from being poisoned.   When the risk of
infection comes from contact with carrion, as may easily
occur in shafts used as charnel houses, it is serious.   I
myself have partially lost the use of two fingers of my
right hand from not having worn gloves, the result of a
septic wound I got from a contact of this kind in the
Gouffre de Cagire in Haute-Garonne.

Lighting

Even now, attired from top to toe, a spelaeologist to the
finger-tips, and longing to learn more about caves, there is
nothing to be done while one essential thing is still lacking,
the lamp, without which no one must enter the realms of
darkness.   The aviator has his wings and his parachute,
the sailor his lifeboat and his buoys, the diver his supply
of air.   Who is to supply the spelaeologist's greatest need
and bestow on him a really adequate means of lighting his

way? This problem of primary importance is still in the early stages of solution. Only too often the explorer suggests a feeble glow-worm in the thick darkness in which he crawls, and the best lamp tried up to the present is but a makeshift affair. Nevertheless, this matter of lighting should receive the greatest possible attention and care from those who hope to do pioneering work in caves.

Let us first take out of this box containing a whole pile of my various contrivances for lighting, the simplest, dimmest, and surest of all, the humble candle.

Admittedly, a candle gives but a faint light, which dazzles the bearer, yet hardly reaches beyond his feet; but it is *par excellence* the emergency light, which is always ready, and burns to the very last morsel, and which nothing, not even water, can damage. If a candle drops into the water, it has the merit of floating and it can be lit again after being hung up to dry. A spare candle should always be carried to provide against the possible breakdown of acetylene and electric lamps, which are the normal types used by exploring parties.

Acetylene lamps, of which I possess several types, have this advantage that they give a light which lasts a long time and is cheap; a handful of calcium carbide will give an adequate light for ten or twelve hours. But when it comes to climbing walls or to spells of ladder climbing, the acetylene lamp must be put out and fixed to the belt, and replaced by the electric lamp on the forehead.

This lamp in the helmet is fed from a dry battery (kept in a pocket) through a wire which goes down beside the chin-strap and under the neck of the overall, and so is not liable to catch in anything. Lighting from the forehead is good, because it leaves both hands free and throws the light in the direction in which you are looking. An electric pocket-lamp or torch with a variable focus is also of great use, as it enables one to illuminate holes a long way down or to examine the details of roofs up to heights of nearly two hundred and fifty feet. Whatever sort of battery is used this type of lamp is costly, its brightness diminishes rather rapidly, and it does not last long enough to be used continuously.

That is why I give the preference to the acetylene lamp, which every user is studying to improve by constant alterations in the method of attaching it, in the reflector, and in the calibre of the jet. It is my faithful companion with whom I push on underground, to explore and discover everything I can. It lights up walls, rows of galleries, and vast halls which had never seen the light before, and which relapse into perpetual darkness once its fleeting beam has passed. At all times and in all places it is held and moved about with the respect that is its due, and the bearer is more careful of it than of his own person, for on it will depend, from beginning to end, the success of the expedition, and it will be thanks to its guiding light that he will thread his way through the dark and intricate tunnels and eventually return to the surface.

Despite every precaution, the lamp is occasionally extinguished by a knock or a fall or a strong draught and has to be lit again.

One thinks nothing of this happening in other places, but underground, for a man alone, it is invested with a solemnity which the most hardened explorer cannot shake off. If you have never known the absolute darkness, the oppressive silence, which suddenly fall upon you and threaten you directly the flame of your lamp goes out, you cannot conceive the plight of the man who finds, when it happens, that he has been fool enough to come without matches or lighter.

Provision against such an accident is essential; that is why the small handbag which, like the lamp, accompanies me everywhere must contain, before all else, matches and a lighter. It is as well to carry an extra lighter and a reserve of matches, just in case the bag is lost, which may happen by its falling into a crevice or down a hole or through being mislaid.

The lighter should be in a pocket of the overall within easy reach, and tied in with a leather strap; the matches should be stuffed into an inside pocket. The latter are only there in case the lighters fail and are practically never used; they are a spare light for an emergency. My colleague de Joly has given much attention to this question of equipment, studying and thinking out its details in the light of long experience, and he rightly recommends only lighters that work automatically and not by pressing the finger on the small wheel, for the hands are almost always wet or muddy. Matches, I need hardly say, should not be left in the box you buy them in, where they would quickly become unusable. A waterproof metal box or rubber case is needed to keep them dry. I possess two cases which are perfect for the job and exactly similar, though I got them in quite different ways. For years I had been using cases that were not absolutely watertight till one day in Saint-Jean-de-Luz I passed a shop that sold swimming gear, and there, conspicuously displayed, I saw cigarette cases for swimmers. An illustrated advertisement showed a lady about to enter the water with one of these cases in the belt of her costume. A second photograph showed the same fair swimmer sitting on a rock far out at sea ecstatically enjoying a cigarette she had taken from the case, whose waterproof qualities were strictly guaranteed. The case itself, painted in bright colours, seemed to me a remarkable invention, and I decided to buy a couple on the spot and use them as match-boxes in caves. But the invention being entirely new and of a unique pattern, and the shop being a luxury shop, I had to pay an exorbitant price for even one case.

Some months later I saw in a big Paris shop, no longer in a place of honour, but in a miscellaneous collection, a whole lot of these same cases which had missed fire, and were being sold off far below the actual value for 3·50 francs each! *Sic transit* . . .

These watertight match-boxes gave me complete security

in caves, for though the lighters are very practical and usually act quickly, something occasionally goes wrong, either with the petrol or the stone or the wheel; whereas matches, provided they are dry, are the surest possible light to keep as a reserve.

IMPEDIMENTA

My stout linen bag is white. That may surprise you seeing how it is perpetually trailed, and meant to be trailed, in the mud. Its comparatively white surface helps to make it stand out and catch the eye in the obscurity of caves on the many occasions when it has to be left for a time while various acrobatics are necessary. In caves a khaki-coloured bag could not be detected on the ground only a few feet away. Gloves, which are frequently taken off when underground, all end by being lost in this way, their colour giving them a most unfortunate resemblance to bits of earth.

My bag, when packed for a stay underground, contains various essential or useful articles, which would generally be far safer in one's pockets, but which cannot be put there for fear of making them bulge too much. An inventory of its contents will usually show a compass, though it is seldom of much use except when an accurately oriented plan of the cave is wanted, and a whistle that is loud and preferably of deep tone. Shrill sounds that seem more piercing do not carry far in subterranean passages. This whistle is hung to a cord round my neck and keeps me in communication with friends and helpers when I have to make vertical descents of shafts. By using a previously arranged code of simple signals, we can by this means converse and send messages in places where distance and sound interference and amplification of the echoes make any attempt to signal with the voice quite futile. A knife and some string are always useful. To take soundings of deep crevices and shafts, one must have a sounding line; the sort of reel used in fishing or kite-flying with a weight hung on does very well.

To take soundings of a deep hole by throwing down stones and trying to calculate the depth from the time they take to reach the bottom is now recognized to be a fundamentally unsound method. No account can be taken of the slowing down whenever the stone rebounds from the sides, or of the showers of stones it may dislodge, or of the echoes which prolong the sound, with the result that the real depth of hollows sounded in this way is multiplied many times over.

Into the bag must also go the camera, if you want to bring back pictures of what you have seen or of features you wish to examine at leisure. Photography underground needs long experience and special methods, which involve too much detail to describe here, but it is advisable to use none but the lightest and most easily carried type. You need a stand that folds up in a strong protecting case, otherwise it will quickly become useless, and a supply of magnesium powder is also indispensable. A smokeless illuminating powder can now be bought, which is a great step forward; before that, the burning magnesium gave off a suffocating cloud of smoke which filled the cave and hung about, so that the only escape from it was in flight, supposing you were lucky enough to find the way out!

My own camera has seen fifteen years' service and has had some strange experiences; its bellows have frequently been holed by particles of incandescent magnesium, but its round eye has been concentrated on many scenes no human eye had seen before, and it has made records of hundreds of them.

Two or three newspapers folded at the bottom of the bag take up little room and hardly add to the weight. When torn into narrow strips, they provide most efficient way-markings in a maze of passages. Placed conveniently on the ground at forks or particularly puzzling points they always enable you to pick up the right direction; they are the 'Hop-o'-my-thumb's pebbles' of the spelaeologist. Long thin curls of paper may also be used, but newspapers are better, for they make useful wrappings for such things as mineral specimens, details of archaeological interest, or bones, and at a pinch they make extra coverings against the cold and damp, if a long stay has to be made in the same spot. They are valuable, too, as torches to be lighted and thrown down open pot-holes, where they whirl about and light up the walls.

I find my bag is not always able to hold all the stuff I would like to take, and I often supplement it by carrying a rucksack, which is burdensome and particularly tiresome in crawling or climbing, when it has to be towed along with a bit of cord.

And however one may resent being burdened with such tools, my bag often contains a hammer and chisel; they are indispensable for widening a narrow passage and breaking down columns or stalactites that obstruct a cat-hole.

In pleasant contrast, my blue indelible pencil in its aluminium case is nice and light; it only comes out on great occasions, at the bottom of deep holes or at the very end of great caverns. There, a few modest inscriptions with just a name and a date will endure for hundreds and thousands of years, and presumably will survive the proudest monuments and a whole succession of civilizations, as have the drawings made in the depths of caves in prehistoric times, which still amaze us by their freshness.

Finally, we have here in a flat metal box, alongside a small thermometer for taking air and water temperatures underground, a few bars of chocolate and lumps of sugar, to ease the pangs of hunger and keep me going when I have been too long without food and am ready to drop. They are for occasions when a long stay is not expected and provisions have not been taken. If the necessary provisions and refills of calcium carbide have been taken, a long stay can be made underground, if you do not mind shivering through the hours, if not of sleep, of inaction. Thus provided you should be able to cover several miles;

but it is seldom possible to make long advances without coming up against all sorts of obstacles which are impassable without the proper apparatus which constitutes a spelaeologist's outfit in the strict sense of the word. All I have said above deals simply with the individual's own dress and equipment.

TACKLE

The apparatus used by É.-A. Martel, the first man to carry out a systematic exploration of French caves in 1888, weighed many hundredweight and had to be transported in a cart or on the backs of mules. A numerous team was needed to handle and work it.

The apparatus which does the same job for me, and which you see in a pile there on the floor of the attic, is a much lighter type, the whole thing weighing under one and a half hundredweight. The whole of this tackle has been invented and manufactured by R. de Joly, who has had great experience in underground work. He has aimed at reducing the bulk and weight of ladders without seriously affecting their strength. His calculations and experiments have enabled him to produce ladders whose sides are no longer like thick cables, and whose rungs are not great bars far wider than necessary, but sticks of ash no wider than the foot. His endeavours to find ladders still lighter and easier to handle led him to invent and produce a tackle in steel thread with a section of about one-eighth of an inch, with hollow rungs made of electron. These metal ladders are amazingly strong, made in types weighing only from two and three-quarters to three and a half ounces per yard. All these spider-line ladders, of which I have a fine supply, can be joined together in a moment by an extremely practical system of linking. As you see them on the floor, done up in small tight rolls, they do not occupy much space, but there are enough there to take me down a vertical shaft of more than sixteen hundred feet.

The technique of such long descents, which I cannot go into now, involves, beside the ladders, the use of ropes, belts, winding gear, pulleys, miniature telephone, etc., all part of my outfit; and for all of its various parts I have to thank the inventive genius of the explorer de Joly. In this way he has bestowed on spelaeologists a remarkable set of tools, which has given new life to the art of exploring deep chasms, just as he has given new life to the Société Spéléologique de France, over whose fortunes he has presided for the last ten years.

It might well seem a thankless, if not impossible task, to discourse about a few hundred yards of ladders and ropes, and I do not mean to try. But each of these same ladders has its special characteristics, its weight, its breadth, and its special use; I know them so well that even in the dark I know which section of them holds me swaying in space. Each has its story and to each a memory clings. A splicing here recalls some adventure, and the mark of a burn there evokes some exciting incident.

Among all this pile of working gear, it may seem odd to find a pair of bellows and a couple of objects that look like ping-pong bats; you might think they had nothing to do with spelaeology and had got stowed away here in the attic. Far from it, the bellows belong to the rubber boat and the bats or mud-shoes are the paddles for propelling my skiff over underground waters. The boat itself is not here where light and heat might damage it, it hangs in the cellar, where the cool air and absence of light help to preserve it. It is four feet long by two feet broad when inflated. When deflated and rolled up it is not at all bulky and goes into a rucksack. The value of a boat like this, weighing only eleven pounds, is inestimable for getting about on water in caves, and nothing could take its place.

This strange form, hanging on the same wire as the rubber boat and likewise kept separate from the other gear, is my diving dress. It is an invention we spelaeologists owe to my friend and fellow explorer Max Cosyns, one of the best things his ingenious brain has given us; a watertight suit without a helmet, consisting of a mackintoshed overall, which slips on over the clothes, leaving nothing exposed except the head and hands. It fits tightly at the neck and wrists, so that no water can get in. Once inside this watertight dress you are unsinkable, because of the air enclosed which buoys you up, and besides keeping the water out keeps out the cold.

The thing weighs just over a pound and a half; it is made of balloon cloth, as thin as a handkerchief but very strong, the lightest of diving dresses, which in no way interferes with the movement of the body. At the same time, a thin skin like this is not meant to be scraped against rough walls or sharp rocks, so it is advisable to put the boots on over it and then the usual cave overall. Thus clad, the diver is completely covered up and protected, and it is great fun to plunge fully dressed into an underground stream, even in winter, to the amazement of friends or sightseers, who fail to realize that the overall and boots are the only things which the water penetrates. If only I had known of this wonderful diving dress for caves fifteen years earlier, I should have been spared the horrible times I have spent with chattering teeth in icy water, and I should have doubtless also avoided the rheumatism that is coming to me in the future, and which, when it has me in its grip, will cause me no surprise and will leave me in no sort of doubt as to how I invited its attack.

The description of my tackle shall end here, and I beg your forgiveness once more for having talked so much about myself, saying and repeating, like the pigeon in La Fontaine's tale: 'J'étais là, telle chose m'advint, vous y croirez être vous-même.' My excuse is that I did not want to describe anything with which I was not myself familiar, that the advice I have given is based on personal experience, and that I have told you only what I have seen and what I have actually done, things of which I have often been the only witness.

I hope what I have written has achieved my object, to be of some use to those who want to go down below, and to have satisfied the curiosity of those who want to know something of the practical side of spelaeology.

That is my last wish, as we take a final look round at all this tackle and equipment, and shut the door of this attic, which, in addition to a strong smell of hemp and clay, lets forth a host of memories: of landscapes, adventures, and of unforgettable emotions which succeeding years have brought me and which have accumulated in this dark retreat.

Later, when my exploring days are over, it is here, I am sure, that I shall come to recall those memories. Under the sun-baked tiles, listening to the friendly sparrows hopping and twittering about the roof, I shall come to enjoy my dreams and thank God for having given me a love of the regions underground, and for having permitted me to discover and marvel at some of the wonders they contain.

4

THREE YEARS WITH THE BATS

. . . ne recevoir jamais aucune chose pour vrai que je ne la connusse
évidemment être telle; c'est-à-dire éviter soigneusement la
Précipitation et la Prévention. . . .[1]

DESCARTES, *Discours de la méthode.*

Bats, known to zoologists as chiroptera or cheiroptera, are the only mammals that fly, and are distributed over the whole world, even as far as and beyond the Arctic circle. Roughly speaking, they can be divided into mega-chiroptera and microchiroptera. The latter, the smaller chiroptera, are the only sort found in France, where they are represented by seven genera totalling twenty different species.

Little is known about the bat and even less of what is to its credit, though it is quite common in France. It inspires a strong feeling of repulsion, one might almost say of terror, yet it is an entirely inoffensive creature; it is loaded with abuse and accused of all kinds of misdeeds, when in actual fact it is wholly and eminently useful. In another book I have written at length my views on the ingrained but erroneous tales which have been circulated to its detriment.

It has not been difficult to rectify certain errors and clear the character of this little animal, and I ventured to suggest that it might be an object for men's goodwill and gratitude by reminding them that it was by studying the flight of chiroptera and the structure of their wings that Clément Ader got his ideas for the construction of his 'bat' aeroplane with wings that beat. And it was with

[1] Nothing must be accepted as true till it has been clearly recognized as being so; which means that every care must be taken to avoid haste and prejudice. . . .

BAT-CATCHING WITH THE NET

this 'heavier than air' machine that the Father of Aviation realized the proudest of man's dreams and the most wonderful invention of all time: flying in space. . . .

But I have not yet told the whole story of the bat; a single chapter was not enough. Therefore I am coming back to this creature, for which I have a special regard, I suppose because it is the only one that frequents caves and because I love to see how it flies about and lives there. I have been thrilled and am still amazed by my study of it, for few animals have such extraordinary habits and behaviour.

Are bats sedentary animals, living in caves and only venturing out, when night comes, within a short radius of the cave which is their refuge? That has long been the accepted view; but these weird creatures had many baffling surprises in store for the naturalists, and if it is true that a few of the species appear to be great stay-at-homes, others are very great travellers and make seasonal migrations.

The best way to investigate this last matter is to make systematic observations of the bats in a given cave, taking careful notes of their behaviour through a period of twelve consecutive months. That is what I have been doing for several years, and thanks to these hitherto unpublished notes I shall be in a position to give some precise details about the habits and migrations of our Pyrenean bats.

To give the reader some idea of the conditions and atmosphere in which I do my observing, I cannot do better than invite him to come with me into one of these caves, that we may explore it and spy out everything that happens in the course of a year. The cave of our choice is called the Grotte des Tignahustes, a strange name but prophetic, seeing that the word means bats in the patois of the Hautes-Pyrénées.

It is situated in the department of Hautes-Pyrénées, not far from Montrejeau and Saint-Bertrand-de-Comminges, within a few hundred yards of the famous prehistoric cave of Gargas, one of the earliest in the Pyrenees to be

K

discovered, studied, and listed among the ancient monuments of France. It has now been made easy of access
and lighted by electricity, so that any tourist can admire its
halls hung with stalactites and the remarkable evidences of
previous occupation by cave-men, in particular certain
strange impressions of mutilated hands depicted on the
walls and known as the *mains-fantômes* of Gargas.

In contrast with the Gargas cave, which is at the end of
a motor road, the Grotte des Tignahustes is little known
and seldom visited; its entrance is on the mountain-side,
deep in the forest, a mere opening in the ground concealed
by undergrowth and most uninviting. You have to bend
very low to get in, and then go down a steeply inclined
shale slope, which ends in a chamber of no great size and
of no special interest.

Roofs and walls are bare and gloomy, unadorned with
any stalactites; it is a very ordinary cave with a boulder-
covered floor. The first discovery revealed by a tour of
inspection is a passage some twenty yards long leading to
a dead end, then comes another passage with a very low
roof, where you have to do an unpleasant crawl in filthy,
smelly mud. Once through this, it is possible to stand up
again and proceed into a second chamber pervaded by the
characteristic smell of bat guano. In fact, the first thing
one notices is a heap of guano kept liquid by a trickle of
water, the effluent being carried by the slope of the ground
into the narrow passage by which you have had to worm
your way from the first chamber to the second. The
latter, which marks the end of the cave, is rather the bigger
of the two, with a higher roof, but equally devoid of interest.
Not without interest, however, for the bats, who have
made it their abode, it may be for centuries, as is evidenced
by the formidable deposits of guano.

Not that this cave of Tignahustes is one of those, such as
are found in hot countries, in which the accumulations of
excrement baffle description. I have explored many guano
caves in Africa, and I fear I should be accused of exaggera-

tion if I described what I have seen. I will, nevertheless, quote from the striking account given by an expert entomologist, Professor Jeannel, who has visited innumerable caves in all parts of the world in the course of his researches on insects that infest caves. 'When you enter a guano cave,' he writes, 'the first thing that strikes you is an intolerably strong, bitter smell, a mixture of the smell of the bat and that due to ammoniacal fermentation. The atmosphere feels warm and damp. Despite the light shed by the lamps, the darkness seems impenetrable, the ground being black with guano. The roof is black with bats, many of which are flitting about in all directions, filling the place with their cries and the muffled whirring of their wings. In their wild, panicky flight they collide with the visitor and his lamps, which are extinguished. Clusters of the creatures crowd up against the roof, where they fight to get a hold, as there is not always room for them all. Some of them, dislodged when asleep, have fallen to the ground, where they crawl about with wings outspread; here and there baby bats that have dropped off their mothers' teats show up in tiny white patches on the black floor.

'As he advances the visitor has to climb hillocks of guano, in which he may be knee-deep. In places he may find a rock to give him foothold, but it is hard to see what is rock, the surface is so completely covered with a layer of stinking slime. Insects, myriapods, scuttle about in all directions; clouds of diptera flutter in the air, and the guano itself seems sometimes to be alive, as it heaves up and down with the movement of millions of insects that live in it. In a cave in Algeria, El Ghar, there were millions of ptinides moving about in the guano. In East Africa, in the caves of Shimoni, I have seen thousands of great cockroaches plunging violently in the middle of the heaps and imparting to them a wave-like motion. These swarms of insects that live on guano are often equally great in the temperate zone, as in the Pyrenean cave of Izeste at Arudy.'

The Grotte des Tignahustes, to which we will now return, does not present the same appearance as the above. For seven months of the year it is deserted and only occupied by the bats for the remaining five. This seasonal occupation, which I had noticed long before in this and several other caves, made me curious to know the reasons for it and led to my making a systematic study of bats; I chose the Tignahustes caves for the scene of the experiments I made in order to learn more about their habits.

It is not every cave that offers opportunities for observation, for all caves do not contain bats; in only a few, in fact, are they found in any great numbers. My reason for choosing Tignahustes was its isolated position and its lack of spectacular attractions, which left it quite free from visitors, and gave me every chance of being able to work in peace.

It was a day in November when I began my observations. The two chambers in the cave only provided ten or a dozen bats to observe of the rhinoloph species known as 'horse-shoe' which are to be found in almost any cave, cellar, or barn.

In the second chamber the hill of guano was, as I had already ascertained, a proof that it had been inhabited for a long time by a big colony; but how long had the cave been abandoned? Had it been definitely abandoned, or might it be that the colony had migrated and might one day return?

The winter gave me no fresh data to go upon. The only result of my observing was to learn that the few rhinolophs I had seen in November remained in the place all through the winter, hanging separately, head downwards and wrapped up in their wings in a state of absolute torpor.

At last on 5th April, when my patience was becoming sorely tried, my persistence was rewarded. Directly I entered the cave I became aware of a vast number of small shrill squeaks, which guided me to the second chamber

VIEW FROM TIGNAHUSTES

where it is always pitch dark.   On the roof, about twenty-five feet above me, my lamp showed me a large colony of bats packed close together.   A few yards away from the main swarm, two or three other clusters appeared as tawny patches of swarming life the roof.   The migrants had evidently returned and were evincing great excitement at being disturbed.   They had no suspicion of the troubles in store for them through my attentions in the ensuing months, and I myself had no idea then of the extent to which these small creatures were to absorb my interest.

On this first day, I had to be content with observing the colony from a distance and asking myself a question I have not yet managed to answer: Where did it come from? I was on the spot again next day with a contrivance I had made myself; it was a broad, deep sort of butterfly net of linen, which I hoped, when I fixed it to a long handle, would enable me to reach the swarm clinging to the roof. The device proved a huge success, for in two sweeps I netted two hundred and twenty-five bats.

From an examination of this first collection I discovered that the colony was made up of two quite different species: murinae and minioptera.   The murinae are the biggest bats we have in France; they have a nose like a fox and big ears, and the wings may have a spread of as much as sixteen inches.   The minioptera, on the other hand, are small creatures weighing barely one-third of an ounce; the nose is flattened like a pug's, and the wings are tapered, enabling them to fly with amazing rapidity.

Laden with my booty, which heaved and protested in the net, I sat down in the entrance to the cave in the daylight and set about ringing my small prisoners with a special kind of aluminium clasp, on each of which was stamped a different designation, as well as the words: 'Museum Paris.'

The ringing was done by putting a thin aluminium cylinder with a slit parallel to the axis round the bat's foreleg, then gently closing it up with the thumb and forefinger. If the operation is well done, the bat will never lose the ring or be hurt by it, as it will slip easily up and down the limb.

The first bout of ringing, dealing with over two hundred cases, was a lengthy and delicate bit of work. The minioptera struggled madly, screaming and biting all the time; the bites were particularly unpleasant, as the jaws and sharp teeth were so formed as to make it impossible for them to let go; it was necessary to force open the mouth to get free. The murinae were less violent and less vicious, uttering loud squeals and being less clever at biting; but when they get hold of a finger they draw blood. As I released my victims, they disappeared without hesitation into the cave to swell the swarm which I had momentarily dispersed with my net and which was re-forming on the roof.

The arrival of all these migratory bats with the swarming instinct coincided with the disappearance of the few rhinolophs which had spent the cold season at Tignahustes in a deep sleep and hanging separated from one another. It can be imagined how the latter, with no instinct for close association and their wild fierce nature, must have been upset and put to flight by the advent of a great colony of intruders.

I now paid daily visits to the cave in my eagerness to observe this multitude of newcomers. At any time of the day, I found the swarm clinging close together and comparatively quiet; not a single bat broke away, and a few faint twitterings were the only sound I heard. Although changes in temperature and other weather conditions produced no corresponding effects in the inner parts of the cave, I found that the swarm was much quieter and more inert on days when there was wind or rain and when it was colder outside. Some days indeed, even the bagging in the net and the beginning of the ringing process failed to rouse them from their torpor. The minioptera were particularly inert, and did not fly off at once when I let them go. Once well awake, however, they showed themselves, as usual, much livelier and more inclined to bite than the murinae.

When it was fine and warm outside the cave, my entrance was greeted by protests which got louder and louder. The light from my electric pocket-lamp, dim and purposely screened as it was, speedily produced a great stir in the swarm, which completely broke up. The bats began to flit all round the place uttering squeals of terror, but they never left the cave nor even the inner chamber.

I soon realized that my daytime observations of creatures of the night were leading nowhere, and were only producing unnatural behaviour, and might even lead to the abandonment of the cave. I therefore decided to pursue my inquiries at night. Obviously, it was not going to be an easy job, but I was determined not to be beaten, and set about studying my bats without their being aware of it, in silence and darkness.

There was only one possible way, to station myself at the entrance to the cave and watch the nightly departures and returns. I did this and am still doing it, keeping long solitary vigils which are not without their trials, but are a fruitful source of information and have also a certain fascination.

From these vigils I have learned all there is to know about the times when bats leave their homes and return to them. I take up my position by the porch of the cave and keep a close watch on what goes out or in. I have no light and keep perfectly still, and no smoking is possible, for bats have an extremely keen sense of smell. I have kept in this way an exact record of entries and exits, the rhythmic machinery of which seemed to me of sufficient interest to give the reader, for there are no previous records of observations of the kind.

I will not weary you with a minutely detailed list of the incidents which marked this long series of night vigils; I will take just one of the most typical that occurred on the night of 27th–28th May 1938.

I am sitting on a patch of shale on the mountain-side, just before sunset, within a few yards of the entrance to the cave. From my perch my eyes can roam over a characteristic stretch of Pyrenean country. Being on a buttress of the main chain, my prospect includes to east and west the final slopes where the Petits Pyrénées descend to the banks of the Nesle and the Garonne, which meet in the centre of the view. Beyond these two rivers to the north the ground rises into the vast spreading uplands of alluvial soil which form the plateau of Lannemezan and fans out in the far distance into Gascony. On it are outlined the small towns of Saint-Gaudens, Montrejeau, and Lannemezan, while nearer villages can be seen scattered about in the valley. The Grotte des Tignahustes, about one thousand eight hundred feet above the sea, where the mountains begin to merge into the plains, is well placed for a view of the woods and meadows which are the bats' happy hunting grounds.

From my high vantage ground I overlook the country-side, where the sounds of life are gradually diminishing and dying away. Carts are slowly climbing the hill below the village of Aventignan, whose church spire stands up against the light in the west. A flock of sheep is making its way home over the open ground, shepherded by a dog which I can faintly hear barking as it hustles them along. I would like to stay on looking at the scene till twilight ends, but the moment of my watch has come and I must tear myself away. So I turn into the undergrowth and settle down by the entrance of the cave, getting there just as the sun sets, that is to say about 8.20 by official summer time.

My preparations for the night do not take long, as I carry up the minimum I consider necessary. A water-proof sheet is first spread out on the ground to keep off the damp, then I lie down full length upon it on my back with my feet and legs inside the cave, my head and chest outside it, and my eyes looking up at the sky.

My working outfit consists of a small notebook, a pencil,

and a wrist-watch with a luminous dial. An electric torch, for getting about in the cave if I want to, is all I have besides. I am now ready, my vigil is beginning; I have lost the wonderful panorama of Comminges now passing slowly into the peaceful slumber of night. My view is confined to a bit of rocky roof and a patch of sky that grows darker and darker as I watch it. Lying here with foliage all round me, half in and half out of the cave, sounds from the outer world hardly reach me at all; I hear nothing but the ceaseless drip, drip of the water that collects on the roof of the cave. Not far off, however, I know the bushes are still awake with a blackbird's evening song and the 'tit-tit' of a robin.

My thoughts have turned to bats asleep underground, hanging from the dark vaultings of the second chamber, which will soon awake, on this evening as on others, from their torpor and fly out into the night through the cave door to take possession till dawn of the realm abandoned to them by the birds, cleaving their invisible tracks across it. What sort of instinct, what mysterious sense is it, which tells these creatures living buried underground, sometimes at great distances and depths from the exit, that night has succeeded day? How do they know that the wind and rain they dread are raging outside, in which case they do not stir from where they are all night?

The robin and a wren are moving about in the thicket near me. A couple of blackbirds, whose last whistling notes have just broken the hush of evening, have returned to covert in the undergrowth, where I can hear the dry leaves rustling under their feet as they settle down. Night comes on and a few stars show points of light. All is hushed in a universal calm.

Suddenly I gave a start, for I heard a sort of whirring by my feet and three dark shadows whistled through the air a few inches from my face. The first three bats with their strong, rapid flight had just darted out of the cave on their way to the sleeping plain below. My immediate reaction was to jot down three strokes in my notebook and I remained on the alert, for the nightly procession about to begin would soon become a rush, when eye and hand would have to act quickly. My notebook was all ready, with a page for each five minutes of observation. The first page was headed 8.30 to 8.35, the second 8.35 to 8.40, and so on. It only remained for me to put down so many strokes for the number of bats seen, while a glance at the luminous dial of my watch showed me when to begin a fresh page.

By this means I could keep an accurate check on the number of bats that passed out flying within inches of my eyes under the low arch and silhouetted for a fraction of a second against the pale ashen screen of sky.

Feverishly I noted down the swift rush of each one, and could feel the beat of its wings as it passed over me. As far as I could, I made a different mark for the powerful flying murinae and the darting minioptera, but there was not always time, for the rush of bats was working up to a climax.

Here is the record for this nocturnal exodus for periods of five minutes, beginning with the first lot of three bats: 5, 11, 14, 25, 63, 135, 197, 260. After reaching this maximum the rate diminishes: 131, 58, 16, 4.

After 9.35 I stopped recording the exits. Quite exhausted by the strain of writing and watching through this hour of flight, I sat down, and by the light of my torch I counted the score scribbled all over the notebook. It looked like a page of strokes written in a copybook by a child of four! A few of them overlapped, but I managed to count nine hundred and twenty. That seems to give a total of nine hundred and twenty for the present population of the Grotte des Tignahustes.

I let several minutes elapse; nothing more flew out. The cave should be entirely deserted and I should be able to go in without disturbing anything beyond a few bats that might have lagged behind or were ill. Passing through the first chamber, I made my way into the second; I turned my torch up and lit up the bare roof; there was not a sign of a bat.

At that moment, then, the whole colony was out in the woods and meadows, hunting for the insects which fly about in myriads on a fine night in May and provide hecatombs of victims for the bats.

Sitting down on a rock I got together some of my notes and tried to account for the peculiar features of this strange nightly exodus. The first three bats—the scouts of the colony—left the cave twenty minutes after the sun had set; the last four did not pass the entrance till an hour and a quarter after sunset. Why this long interval, and how explain the gradual increase and subsequent decrease in the numbers flying out? Why do the bats not come out in one huge flight, as for example, a flock of birds do?

I can give no sure explanation and can only offer a suggested reason, for it is not possible to be actually present when the swarm breaks up in the usual way. If, as I tried to do several times, one attempts to get a sight of the daily departure of the swarm from its sleeping place, it is obviously necessary to have a light; and, however dim that light may be, it is sufficient to spread panic among the swarming bats and they break up in a few seconds.

A likely explanation of the remarkable duration and the machinery of this normal manner of leaving the cave was one day suggested to me by a scene which appeared to have no sort of connection with the subject; the sight of some children running after ducks! Ducks, as we all know, are made to swim on the water; and children, being logical beings, object to seeing them on dry land. So, one day, as my children were passing a pond, beside which several ducks were enjoying a peaceful sleep, they proceeded to wake them up and get them back into their natural element. The ducks, suddenly roused from their pleasant siesta, were in no hurry to get into the pond. For the moment, they even evinced a decided dislike to bathing, and tried to dodge and make off altogether; but the invading party got round them and won the day. Only under dire constraint and rather frightened, despite their webbed feet, the ducks entered the water, where they were evidently ill at ease.

Directly the children had gone, I saw the ducks make for the shore, hurry out of the water, flap their wings, give one or two hoarse quacks, and then proceed to make an elaborate toilet, smoothing their wings down over and over again with their beaks.

It was then that I noticed a thing I knew of but had quite forgotten, that these birds are constantly rubbing the end of the beak on the upper part of the back, and there collecting an oil secreted by special glands, which they use to put a gloss on their feathers and waterproof them. Every one must have seen ducks, geese, and swans getting ready in this way to go on the water. It makes the body more buoyant and insulates it from impregnation and chilling by the water. I saw now why the ducks, suddenly woken up when unoiled, had shown such a reluctance to enter the pond. It is quite possible that a duck whose feathers had lost their grease and could not utilize oil from its glands would get its plumage soaked and ride heavily on the water.

Now I had noticed one evening a small common bat going through some lengthy process I had not understood, and the explanation of which was only revealed to me subsequently by the episode of the ducks. In the dim half-light of the barn I had been able, without need of a torch, to observe this bat whose movements had so puzzled me.

Hanging head downwards, which is the creature's normal position, it kept folding and unfolding its membranous wings and drawing them with a slow sweeping gesture across its nose. When the operation, a lengthy one, was over, the little creature at once flew off with that velvety flight characteristic of bats when they are not in a close mass or frightened. This bat, before going out on its long daily

A MURIN

RHINOLOPHS HANGING ASLEEP

hunt, had been glazing its wings, just as ducks glaze their under plumage and their wings. Waterfowl do the same thing to avoid becoming *poules mouillées*, losing both their assurance and their sailing powers through their plumage becoming sodden.

Bats glaze and waterproof their alar membranes also to protect them from the cold dry air on certain nights which would dry up and roughen the wings, as well as from the mist and rain which might make them so sodden and heavy that they were unable to fly. Where the bats differ from the ducks is in having the oil glands in the end of the nose between the nostrils.

This long digression does, I think, offer a sound reason for the surprising length of time it takes a colony of bats to leave its home at night. With the gregarious species the swarms are so dense, and the individuals in it so tightly interlocked, that there is no possibility of them all together going through the operations which prepare them for a night's flying. Only those on the outskirts of the swarm have liberty of movement, the first to fly off being a few of these who are less patient and hungrier than the rest. As other departures occur, more individuals are free from their entanglement with the swarm, and can, in their turn, proceed to put a glaze on their wings.

This would explain the exits from Tignahustes in the observed periods of five minutes, beginning at a rate of 3 to 5 bats, reaching a maximum of 200 to 260, then rapidly decreasing to departures of 50, 30, 15, till at the end they are reduced to the solitary exits of a few laggards.

What is there to do, lying out at night like this, but to meditate, and what better surroundings for observing and for thinking than the depths of a cave? It is unfortunately true that cold and damp are drawbacks to a long stay there without moving. I have begun to notice that a drip of icy water from the roof is keeping up a constant patter on my shoulder and seems to be trying to find a way between my coat collar and my neck; the cold nature of the rock I am sitting on has also obtruded itself on my notice.

My watch tells me it is ten-thirty, so I have already spent an hour without moving from this chilly spot.   I picture myself in town at this hour, when the shows are in full swing; the last act, the big film feature, dancing, and the rest.   Presently will come the scrimmage in the cloak-room, the chattering crowd emerging into the street.   How greatly I prefer these caves of mine, where my thoughts are my own, where I can appreciate to the full 'the freedom to do just as I like, the excitement of making unsuspected discoveries on my own, the unexpected surprises, and all the immense benefits that time "wasted" can bestow'; where nothing disturbs the silence but the drops that distil from the roof, breaking with a sort of hesitating tick-tack into the stony, solemn silence that belongs to these regions underground! .

Switching on my electric torch once more, I went back to the entrance and lay down on my bit of sail-cloth to resume my watching, which was soon needed again.   In fact, at ten-forty the first bat came back into the cave at a speed and with a certainty which would amaze any one not familiar with it, that is to say almost every one, for there is rarely either an opportunity or a desire to check the way bats go to bed!   Within five minutes nine murinae had disappeared through the narrow space between the ground and the low arch, where my outstretched body helped to further block the passage.   As regards the minioptera, the speed of their swallow-like flight combined with the darkness hardly allowed me to keep an exact tally, for they darted like a flash across the patch of sky I was watching. Fortunately their flight was so rapid that it made a whistling noise which enabled me to mark off these lightning-like home-comings.

Sometimes, watching on a dark night, when the whistle and rush of their arrival made me blink, I have had a sudden fear that one of these shooting stars might fly

straight into my face, a baseless fear, for among the thousands of bats that have whizzed past me not a single one
has brushed me with the tip of a wing.   I have even on
some occasions made it harder for them not to do so by
raising my hand between the roof and my face; not one
has ever run into it, the small winged acrobats have always
got through without a touch.   It borders on the miraculous,
and must depend on some mysterious sixth sense they
possess.

At one o'clock in the morning, when the returns had
dropped to about 12 to 15 every five minutes, I attempted
to satisfy my curiosity by re-entering the cave to watch
the swarm collecting again.   But the beam of my torch,
screened though it was by two thicknesses of my handkerchief, defeated my object, and I only succeeded in
seeing the colony scatter.   The bats were wide awake and
extremely active at this time of night and flew round and
round the chamber in a great fuss.   I withdrew, so as not
to disturb them any more, and passing through the entrance
I sat down, this time outside on the shale, where I had
waited for sunset a few hours before.

For the first time that night, I let my eyes wander over
the familiar landscape.   Down in the valley, the twinkling
lights in the villages scattered about in the darkness
answered to the starry sky above.   The night express, all
lighted up, moving swiftly along, on its way from Toulouse
to Bayonne, Hendaye, and Spain, where it was due at daybreak, was just climbing up to the plateau of Lannemezan.
In contrast to these evidences of civilized life, the dark
sleeping forests retained their mystery, and in the densest
part of one of them I could locate the position of the prehistoric cavern of Gargas.   Thousands of years ago, it was
inhabited by men who hunted mammoths, bears, and
reindeer, as is proved by the evidence still to be read in
the engravings on the walls.   The peace and solitude
invited me to imagine myself back in these vanished times
and to picture what such a night as this might have been

like some thirty thousand years back, when the whole country was hidden under huge forests, inhabited by ferocious beasts, when the Garonne and the Neste were raging torrents fed by enormous glaciers, which have now disappeared. Even then, the Grotte des Tignahustes may have given shelter to a colony of bats, the remote ancestors of those which this very night were flying to and fro, looking for their nightly meal.

A shrill discordant yelp, not far off in the thicket, interrupted my reverie; some fox on the prowl. A moment later, I detected, only a few yards away, the rustle of trampled twigs and leaves. Was it a fox? The noise was so faint, it sounded more like a weasel or a hedgehog.

That is all that is left of the vanished fauna of the Aurignacian epoch, when gigantic mammoths and lumbering buffaloes had their haunts in this corner of the Pyrenees.

If any man can spend a night alone on the watch in the woods, or on the sea or in the trenches, and never do some dreaming, let him cast the first stone of scorn at me; to me it seems impossible to remain unmoved by the enchantment of a starry night, by the nostalgia that its beauties can evoke.

Two o'clock found me once more prostrate in the entrance to the cave, intent on keeping a careful record, for it was important to find out whether the bats go out twice in a single night. Apparently it is not the case, for only occasional home-comings occurred, and those not frequent or at sufficiently definite intervals to keep me on the stretch. As a result, my attention relaxed, my eyes, tired with scanning for hours the dark patch above them, closed, and the bats continued to come in just missing with their wings the observer now asleep, his notebook and pencil no longer in his hand but on the ground beside him.

At four-thirty I woke up stiff all over and half frozen by the cold draught coming through the entrance. It was cold, day was breaking, and the wood, which seemed to have been emptied of life all night, was already gay with the thrushes' opening song.

Feeling like a sentry who has slept at his post, my first thought was of the bats, to whose doings I had failed to devote a whole night. But I must admit that my feelings of remorse were quickly subdued and pushed aside by the pangs of hunger, a real cave-man's hunger. From my own ravenous appetite I could imagine what our remote ancestors must have felt like, when they woke up after going supperless to bed. When they too had slept and shivered on the hard floor of a cave, they must have woken literally as hungry as wolves!

I can recommend, if not to rheumatic subjects, at least to dyspeptics, a course of nights in the entrance to a cave; it is the best of appetizers!

I did not, all the same, let my ravenous state make me omit a last visit to the bats, whom I found once more reconstituted as a compact colony, but still very restless. It was five o'clock and at the end of the night there was still a good deal of movement going on.

On other nightly vigils similar to the above I found that from April to August, that is during the bats' stay at Tignahustes, they behaved in just the same way. Variations in the times of sunset during the period determine the variations in the time at which the nightly exits begin, which is always from twenty to thirty minutes after the sun has disappeared. The swarm which, we shall see later, may vary from 400 to 1,000, takes from an hour to an hour and a half to vacate the cave; the larger the swarm the longer it takes. The cave remains empty for about two hours.

The return of the bats is a much slower and more irregular affair than the general exodus. The time it occupies evidently depends on the speed and success of the hunt for insects, and this again depends on the meteorological conditions on the particular night, which may or may not favour the hatching out.

L

I did not think it necessary to sacrifice any bats after their nocturnal feast to find out what was in their stomachs; it was enough to know that these extremely useful and greedy creatures spend several hours of the night hunting for their insect food. Flying with open beak like the swallow and nightjar, bats dart about with astonishing skill through the clouds of insects hovering in the air and take them down their open throat, like whales feeding in a plankton in the sea.

Bats are very sensitive to changes of weather, and these affect their behaviour at nights. Cold, wind, and rain restrict and may completely suspend the exodus. Every year, at the beginning of June, I have noticed they leave their homes earlier in the evening; in some cases only ten minutes after sunset. The reason for this is physiological, and brings us to the question of the processes of reproduction among bats, and more particularly among the murinae, of which I know more than of other kinds from having made a prolonged study of them at Tignahustes.

Bats are mammals with a placenta. I venture to remind the reader of this, because it is sometimes forgotten, and I have been asked whether bats make nests and what their eggs are like! But there is one point much less known to those who have not made a study of this exceptional kind of mammal; mating takes place in the autumn, but fertilization does not occur till the beginning of the following spring; a wonderful example of the precautions and care nature shows in thus allowing the male to play his part at the best moment of the year, the end of the period of intense feeding and just before the long winter sleep; whereas gestation in the female only begins with the awakening in the spring, when she can take up her normal active life, produce her offspring and nourish it. The period of gestation is about two and a half months and shows that the murinae arriving at Tignahustes between 25th March and 5th April choose it as their home for the whole period, the young of the colony being born in the early part of June.

I have already pointed out that the Tignahustes colony is a mixture of murinae and minioptera. The latter do not produce their young in the cave, and the length of their stay in it is rather uncertain, so I decided to concentrate my attention and my observations on the murinae.

I have now been ringing these murinae for several years, and thousands of them have passed through my hands, yet not once have I come across a single male, either at Tignahustes or at any other cave, in the Pyrenees. The reason is that the females, as soon as they are fertilized, leave their homes, separating from the males, and set out on a migration, the extent of which I do not know, but which is coincident with the great spring migration of birds.

I have found out that the number of minioptera living with the murinae (presumably in order to benefit by the warmth of numbers, these smaller bats being very sensitive to cold) becomes smaller and smaller as the time of parturition approaches for the murinae. Probably they are then evicted after a pitched battle.

All the small murinae are born about the same time, almost on the same day. Twins are rare and there are never triplets. These baby bats come into the world hairless and with closed eyes; they cling vigorously to the mother's body with the help of their tiny claws and by keeping their mouth tightly fixed to the teats without ever letting go.

For the first months of their existence the young are never separated from the mother, whether she is at rest or in flight. In fact, when night comes, she sets off to hunt with this precious but embarrassing burden, which hampers her freedom of flight and weighs her down. At this time the mothers are particularly hungry and their hunting more arduous, and I have noticed that, in consequence, the murinae go out sooner, sometimes only a few minutes after sunset.

The babies have fierce appetites and suck greedily, and their growth is rapid. In the swarm, whose numbers are

L 2

doubled by the new births, you can sometimes see them crawling over the tangle of bodies, burrowing into the mass with plaintive squeaks, in order to be fed by other females. So highly developed is the herd instinct in these murinae that the mothers appear to have no recognized offspring; my observations of various incidents has pretty well convinced me of this.

When the young bats are twenty-five or thirty days old, they are already so well developed that their nurses are unable to fly with such a heavy burden; so, when night comes, they bite their babies to make them let go. The latter protest loudly and the din is deafening. At last, when they have been duly chastened, that is to say nipped, they cling to the corrugations of the roof and the mothers go off on their nightly flight alone.

For two or three hours the cave then contains nothing but the infant population of the colony. They are a rowdy lot and keep up a continual chirping like that of chicks. The more precocious do wing-extending exercises as if they were impatient to fly, but they take very good care not to let go with their claws. If a young bat falls to the ground it is as good as dead, unless the mothers carry out a rescue, a proceeding I have never been able to confirm. Whether it occurs or not, though occasional falls do certainly happen, I have rarely seen a small corpse lying on the guano heap on the floor. Were these the over-rash or clumsy which had fallen, or were they perhaps some that had died from wounds or sickness?

It is difficult to accept the view that hundreds of nurses on their return from hunting can recognize their own babies in the swarm of small bodies. The probability is that the mother suckles the first-comer, the first occupant of the desired place. The opposite view would imply a remarkable *tour de force* on the part of both mothers and babies, but with bats can one ever be sure? At any rate, I have often separated babes from mothers and entrusted them to other females, and the adoption has followed at

once. This immediate adoption is the more understand-
able because all the females are mothers and nurses at the
same time and consequently the young are of the same age.

At a month and a half the young bats are beginning to
fly and to go hunting at night; but apparently they are not
yet completely weaned.   This mixed diet helps to accelerate
their already rapid development.   They very soon attain to
the size and appearance of the adults and only differ from
them in having a darker coat and a smaller spread of wing.

At two and a half months the adolescents are capable of
long flights, for the time has come for the whole colony to
leave the cave. The males born in the course of the year
will never come back, while the young females will return
there every year with their mothers and, later, with their
daughters.   The colony actually comprises several generations, and at the present stage of my observations I have
confirmed that ringed murinae have been coming back to
Tignahustes for three years.

Tignahustes is therefore a sort of maternity home and
nursery for gestation, birth, suckling, weaning, and the
first flights of the yearly additions to the colony.

In contrast to what happens at the spring arrival, which
is spread over six or seven days, a general departure in a
single night seems to take place about 20th August.   The
extension of the times of arrival over a whole week points,
in my opinion, to the conclusion that the murinae come from
a distance and that some come quicker than others.   Moreover, I noticed that the arrivals coincided with those of the
first swallows in the district.   The coincidence of dates is
worth noting, and led me to make the rather daring
suggestion that bats, both the murinae and the minioptera
are gathered into the great migratory flood, which brings
to us from distant regions in the spring swallows, swifts,
warblers, cuckoos, nightingales, orioles, quails, and turtle-
doves.   The question was raised; it is no longer without
an answer, since a few observers, but those few worthy of
credence, have studied the phenomenon.

A German naturalist, Otto Hepp, had noticed on a fine autumn afternoon in 1890 a number of bats among a flight of swallows crossing the river Main about two hundred feet above it. Otto Hepp was a serious student, but a very old man. No one doubted his sincerity, but it was thought his eyes had played him false.

However, on 25th September 1933 two other German naturalists, von Finkenstein and Schäfer, were amazed to see a similar phenomenon near the small lake of Ullersdorf in Upper Lusatia. In an hour and a half they counted some five hundred bats flying with some house-martins towards the south.

Finally, in October 1935, M. G. Hugues, son of the eminent and late-lamented French naturalist Albert Hugues, detected bats flying with swallows against a dark sky at Romans in Drôme.

These discoveries leave no doubt that certain species of bats are migratory and high-flying travellers.

A priori, it seems unlikely that bats whose flight is known to be of an uncertain nature, like that of a butterfly, can keep up with the swiftest flying birds; but we must remember that the small creatures we see flitting about near our houses in the moonlight are rhinolophs or small pipistrelles, altogether different from accomplished travellers such as murinae, minioptera, and serotines, whose flight is strong, direct, and swift.

Moreover, some idea of the flying range of bats can be given at once by stating a fact which has been established by frequent observations, that bats encountered out at sea must necessarily have covered great distances in uninterrupted flight. Every year bats are seen flying from the coast of the U.S.A. to the Bermudas and returning. The shortest distance between these islands and the mainland is over six hundred miles. Flights of this length suggest the possibility of the migrations which, let us remember, had been in the thoughts of the French experts Trouessart and Albert Hugues. For some years now, in the U.S.A. and in Germany, bats have been ringed in an endeavour to discover the main channels of migration taken.

It is an inquiry beset with many difficulties. A very large number of naturalists ring birds in all parts of the world, and very satisfactory results have followed, thanks to the collaboration of the sportsmen who have killed the ringed birds and communicated valuable information about them; a form of collaboration which is no less active and efficient for being unintentional. This is by no means the case where bats are concerned.

Who wants to go into a cave to ring bats, creatures which people are usually afraid to touch, and later go into this same cave to examine the roof and look for any that have been ringed before? That explains why the study of bat migration has not progressed far and is still rather nebulous.

I have refused to be put off by these drawbacks, but in my own case I have had to tackle the problem in a different way, and carry out experiments in connection with the homing sense of bats by producing artificial migrations; what I have termed *vols de retour* or removal flights.

This proceeding consists in catching some bats in a cave and, after ringing them, releasing them at different places to see if they can find their way home, and so ascertain the maximum distance from which they can get back to the cave they came from.

It was a tricky experiment and only practical experience has shown the reasons for failure when it occurs. There are, in fact, periods when it is little use trying to experiment. At the beginning of their stay in their summer cave, the migrating females must be left alone, otherwise you may put them off remaining there, for they are creatures with a special desire for solitude and silence. Towards the end of their summer stay, there is also a risk of their not coming back, but making straight for their winter quarters. And finally it is unwise to try and move them when the arrival of their babies is approaching or when they are at the stage of carrying or suckling them. The most favourable times are the beginning of May and during July.

It is not enough to choose the best time; the packing of the bats for transit is vitally important. If they are shut up together in a sack or case or cage they get frightened and angry, and struggle, so that very soon fierce battles are started, in the course of which many are killed and others damaged. They must be kept isolated. The way I pack them myself is to put them in a small wicker hamper or basket, each one wrapped in a separate bit of paper, not cramming in too many, but enough to avoid their being jerked about inside.

Ventilation is provided through the gaps in the wicker-work and even through the bits of crumpled paper, which I am careful not to wrap too tight.

In this way any chance of movement is impossible and the victims of my experiment calm down immediately and become torpid in the great heat produced by the number of closely packed bodies. The worst snag in journeys of some length is that bats being exclusively insect-eating animals, feeding only on live prey, they cannot be fed on the way. Indeed, it is useless to try; they refuse any sort of food in such conditions.

This makes it important to get the journey over quickly and not keep them shut up for more than forty-eight hours. The safest plan is to send off any captured bats early in the morning or at the end of the night, that is to say, as soon as possible after their night meal is over, if the night has been mild and calm.

Having taken every precaution to ensure success, it remained to be seen whether the murinae of Tignahustes, whose instinct would lead them along the same old track their migrating ancestors had followed, would be able to find their way home to their cave from quite different directions.

This was the question I was anxious to settle, and I will give you the main results of my experiments. My first trial with bats from Tignahustes was a release of 165 at Saint-Gaudens, a place about ten miles from the cave in a direct line.

These bats had had a few hours' flitting about in my study before being finally sent off. At 9 p.m. when I opened the windows, the colony left and scattered outside, where it was too dark to follow their movements.

Next morning, in some excitement, I entered the Grotte des Tignahustes. With the first sweep of my net I captured a certain number of bats which had been previously ringed, and among them were several whose rings were marked as having been put on the day before. My experiment had succeeded and the small minioptera released at Saint-Gaudens had got to the cave before me.

A second release of a mixed flight of 65 murinae and minioptera was made at Saint-Martory in Haute-Garonne, 22½ miles from Tignahustes. This time, owing to a mishap which I thought would be fatal, the bats all escaped at midday in broiling sunny weather. I had time to see them flying about for a few minutes before disappearing under cover of trees in a park. They had not collected into one group, but were flying singly.

Three days later I was at Tignahustes and caught eight of these bats. Releasing them in broad daylight had not, apparently, had any ill effects, and I did the same thing several times later in order to shorten the period of incarceration for the victims shut up in discomfort in the hamper.

After this I decided to make a big increase in the distance I took them from their home, and one day in May I carried 120 bats to Toulouse, which is over 60 miles away.

They were released the same evening at nine o'clock in the Jardin des Plantes by my friend G. Giscard, of the Société Spéléologique de France. I followed this release with several visits to Tignahustes, but my sweeps with the net gave entirely negative results. Either the distance had been too great or the lights of the town had dazzled and confused the travellers. Possibly also my sweep with the net might not have caught any of the bats back from Toulouse. I persevered and was well rewarded when, a month later, my net collected several murinae that had returned from there.

Not only so, but a chance capture brought in a very interesting bit of information. One of the murinae released at Toulouse was found at Montmaurin in Haute-Garonne, 50 miles from the former and 12½ miles from Tignahustes. This particular bat was therefore on its way home and the most interesting point is that the place where it was caught was in the direct line between Toulouse and Tignahustes. Other captures of bats at points strung out upon the way from different places of release have confirmed the view that on their way back bats fly in a direct line home.

Subsequently, expatriation of bats followed to increasing distances from their homes, not always with equal success. These flights, it is true, were tried with reduced numbers of 20 to 30 bats, dispatched by train to helpful correspondents. The record for this self-sacrificing help is held by the friend who had previously helped me on the memorable occasion in 1931 when I dyed the waters of the upper Garonne to establish its true source. This lady, Mlle de Sède, on her way to Paris from Saint-Gaudens via Tarbes, Bordeaux, Angoulême, was good enough to take with her three parcels of bats, which she was to release at various points of the journey.

And so, at Poitiers, 250 miles from the cave, the passengers in her compartment were astonished to see a girl take a cardboard box from the luggage rack, open it, and shake out of the window things like curl papers from which emerged some enormous bats!

At Tours, nearly 60 miles further on, a similar scene took

place on the platform, to the great amazement of the public, not the least excited being the station-master, at seeing his station suddenly transformed into an aerodrome for bats!

Finally, on her arrival in Paris (to be exact at Neuilly), Mlle de Sède set the last of the bats at liberty at 2 a.m. from the balcony of her room. As she released them one by one, she noted with interest that all of them flew off deliberately southwards, towards the cave that was their home. But it is a very long way from Neuilly to Tignahustes, 410 miles as the crow flies, and I have not yet recaptured any of these ladies from Paris, nor, for the matter of that, from either Tours or Poitiers. That does not mean it will never happen, for every year I come across subjects I have ringed in preceding years and which have been released at all sorts of different places.

Failing any definite results from these homing flights from Paris, Tours, and Poitiers, this threefold experiment did furnish one quite instructive bit of evidence. The bats, which remained silent and peaceful for all the rest of these long journeys, became extremely restless and noisy when the train passed by the Grotte des Tignahustes and through their own familiar hunting grounds. Some special sense of direction, some instinct in these small creatures, seems to have let them know they were near their usual haunts.

Other homing experiments were tried over distances not quite so great, though still considerable. A release of bats at Agen, more than 80 miles away, was crowned with success.

One fine night in July, my friend Germain Gattet released 45 murinae from the top of the battlements of Carcassonne. This flight was particularly interesting, because the creatures might have been confused by having to fly over a part of the country that was very hilly and extremely rich in caves, and therefore likely to make them lose their way, or choose a home in one of the numerous caves open to them. Nevertheless they triumphed over all these difficulties and accomplished this fine homing flight of 93 miles.

On 15th July 1938, at Saint-Jean-de-Luz in Basses-Pyrénées, I released about 40 murinae. Though they had to cross the whole width of the two departments of Basses- and Hautes-Pyrénées with all their hills and caves, 112 miles in a straight line from home, their success, even at this distance was remarkable.

That same year, I liberated a batch of 18 murinae on the shore at Moliet in Landes. It was a stormy day. When I opened the hamper the poor things, exhausted with the long journey and the heat of a sultry day, were panting for breath. For quite a long time they remained on the shore without moving; then they began a laboured flight, beaten down to the earth several times by the strength of the gusts. They looked in such a bad way that I had no hope of a successful end to this trial. Yet after all, these same bats managed to fly across the huge forest of Landes, the hills of the Chalosse, the endless ups and downs of the department of Gers and part of Hautes-Pyrénées and completed this homing flight of 124 miles.

I will end with the record performance to date, an achievement by a detachment of murinae released this time, not on the Atlantic coast, but on the shore of the Mediterranean.

It was 10 p.m. on 28th May when my brother, Dr. Martial Casteret, opened the usual hamper on the beach at Cette. By a most unfortunate coincidence, which boded ill for the flight, the mistral was blowing a gale and the murinae were all pregnant (one of them actually gave birth to a babe in the train before Cette was reached). The prospects, when we made the release, seemed hopeless. Yet, here again, the marvellous instinct of the bats won the battle at all points, triumphing over the violence of the elements, the unfavourable conditions, and the great length of the journey. Several of them, shooting like swallows across the departments of Hérault, Aude, Ariège, Haute-Garonne, found their way to the tiny doorway of their cave hidden in the woods of the Hautes-

Pyrénées, after an odyssey of 165 miles.   It was a thrilling
moment when, one day, after a chance sweep with the net,
I actually read on the tiny rings the numbers of some that
had made such a valiant march across the sky.   Among
them was a veteran wearing ring 9518, which had already
made a successful homing flight from Toulouse, thus
bringing her total up to nearly 230 miles.

These different experiments have therefore provided
ample evidence that certain kinds of bats have a highly
developed sense of direction and remarkable capacities for
flight, which enable them to reach their home after being
removed to all parts of the compass, to places a hundred
miles and more from the place where they were caught.
Tests having succeeded with flights of nearly 180 miles,
there seems to be nothing to prevent the success of other
flights I intend to try over increasingly greater distances.
But one problem remains to be investigated.   Why do
bats migrate at all?

In the case of birds the reason for their migration is
clear enough; in the spring they leave the countries where
summer is too hot to suit their way of life, and in the
autumn they leave the region which becomes too cold in
winter and where they could not find their usual food.
For bats, these reasons do not exist; when they leave their
summer quarters to go to winter quarters that are far
away, it is not to pursue an active life, but to go off into a
long, deep sleep.   In regard to the sedentary species, one
can only marvel at the providential timing of their lethargy.
What would become of bats in winter, seeing that they
feed entirely on insects and that there are then no insects
to eat?   Providence has provided for the case, and the bat
has adapted itself to an apparently impossible situation; it
gives a literal interpretation to the proverb, 'Qui dort,
dîne,' and goes to sleep.   During this profound sleep,
lasting five or six months, the animal's temperature sinks
to that of the cave in which it hangs, sometimes as low as
three or four degrees centigrade; all its natural functions

are slowed down and almost suspended, the heart beating only two or three times in a minute. This exceptional condition calls for special investigation and would provide one of the most curious of all the chapters in the life-history of the bat.

But I cannot go into this now and must confine myself to the still unanswered question: Why do bats undertake a long journey to reach winter quarters where they merely go to sleep, while their own summer caves would provide them with precisely similar conditions of temperature and humidity, as has been proved?

It looks as if the instinct and the senses of these animals, in some ways highly developed, were here at fault.

The reason for their migration is still unknown, but we can well imagine that in the course of ages migration has lost its significance and its utility, and that this curious aberration on the part of the bats is accounted for by the persistence of this instinct through countless generations. A small rodent of central Europe offers a well-known and comparable example. From time to time hamsters will set off in millions, covering hundreds of miles, getting through any obstacles in their path and crossing rivers. When they reach the northern shores of Europe they plunge into the sea and swim straight ahead till the whole vast troop is drowned. With them also, it is the extra-ordinary persistence of an instinct which has led to their destruction, for if we could go back far enough we should find the lands they could then have reached, but which have been submerged for thousands of years.

The life of bats still presents many curious problems, and my observations, very incomplete as they are, are constantly confronting me with hard questions. These problems, like many others connected with the world underground, are never tiresome; rather they are fertile in suggesting further patient and persistent researches in that inexhaustible and wonderful book, the book of nature.

INDEX

INDEX